ENDANGERED SPECIES

ENDANGERED SPECIES

By Robin W. Doughty
and Barbara M. Parmenter
Illustrations by
Angelo Mitchell

Texas Monthly Press
P.O. Box 1569
Austin, Texas 78767

A B C D E F G H

Library of Congress Cataloging-in-Publication Data

Doughty, Robin W.
Endangered species / Robin W. Doughty and Barbara M. Parmenter.
p. cm.
Includes bibliographical references.
ISBN 0-87719-093-3 : $9.95
1. Endangered species—Texas. 2. Nature conservation—Texas.
I. Parmenter, Barbara M, 1958- . II. Title.
QH76.5.T4D68 1989
591.52'9'09764—dc20 89-5226
CIP

Text design by David Timmons

To Floyd Potter (1925–1987)
for his enthusiasm for
the animals and plants of Texas

CONTENTS

	ACKNOWLEDGMENTS	*ix*
	INTRODUCTION	*1*
1	LABELS AND NUMBERS	*9*
2	HUMAN EXPLOITATION AND HABITAT CHANGE	*19*
3	TIMES HAVE CHANGED: *Twentieth-Century Conservation*	*37*
4	THE JURY IS STILL OUT	*57*
5	NEW CONCERNS AND OPPORTUNITIES	*73*
6	THIRSTY TEXAS: *Development and Endangered Water Life*	*99*
7	PLANTS: *Back to Basics*	*117*
8	WILDLIFE IN AN URBAN AGE	*135*
	SOURCES	*141*
	APPENDICES	*147*

ACKNOWLEDGMENTS

We are extremely grateful to a number of specialists on Texas flora and fauna who made many helpful suggestions and commented on the manuscript, which exists solely because of their research. We make no claim to originality; rather, we have consulted publications, perused files and documents, and spoken with experts knowledgeable about particular animals and plants. This book distills what we have learned. It is an attempt to increase public awareness for the plight of dwindling organisms. It seeks also to commend and broaden recognition for those researchers and organizations dedicated to saving this state's aboriginal heritage.

Raymond Neck, biologist with the Texas Parks and Wildlife Department, has been most kind in reading the text and making constructive comments. Likewise, Bruce Thompson and Jackie Poole, of the Texas Parks and Wildlife Department, had many useful ideas and provided vital information, as did David Diamond and Andrew Price, with the Texas Heritage Program. Charles Winkler offered details about the bighorn. Mike Tewes was most kind in supplying information about his research with ocelots. David Mabie added data about the bald eagle. Amos Cooper spoke to us about the status of the American alligator. Catrina Martin, with the Texas Parks and

Wildlife Department, prepared a list of contacts for specific issues. William McClure made a number of excellent comments, and we are grateful to him for the time and effort taken with the text. Another Texas Parks and Wildlife Department biologist, the late Floyd Potter, was most interested and energetic in helping us gather and update information, especially regarding the nongame program in Texas. Without his assistance this project would not have been possible. We shall always remain greatly indebted to him.

Angelo Mitchell supplied pen-and-ink sketches that enliven the text. Staff members in the Department of Geography, University of Texas, Austin, notably Carol Vernon, Beverly Beaty-Benadom, and Cheri Crass, assisted with manuscript preparation. Thank you all.

INTRODUCTION

The plight of rare and endangered animals throughout the world stirs human passions and ignites debates about the value of these life forms. Organizations spring up to save the whales, dolphins, turtles, condors, even bluebirds and purple martins. The opposition dismisses these creatures in trouble as relicts of a bygone era, anachronisms that have failed to keep pace with progress. The argument is understandable when you recognize that our concern for endangered species is a relatively recent and largely urban phenomenon, born little more than a century ago when scientists, nature writers, and other concerned individuals began to protest fashionable trimmings made from the feathers of wild birds and condemned the slaughter of waterfowl, bison, pronghorn antelope, and other game animals by market hunters and recreationists.

In the last 25 years or so, attention has focused on the more insidious and less controllable impacts on wildlife of pollution and habitat loss. Environmentalists argue that our lives, and more so those of our grandchildren, depend on a healthy and complex web of life from which we derive food, clothing, medicines, and other essential needs. A diverse system of species links, from microscopic decomposers and nitrogen fixers through plants and herbivores to carnivores and omnivores like man, is vital in preserving the intricate balance of life. A complexity of living things means a varied gene pool and furnishes us with essentials. But are those knowledgeable, well-intentioned experts doomsday alarmists, or does their viewpoint have merit? Should it persuade us? Clearly, there is still a great deal to learn about the workings of ecological systems, but the pace of animal and plant extinction is surely accelerating. The growth of human populations and economies has a devastating impact on many aboriginal wildlife species. Although hounded by experts in the industrial and agricultural sectors, biologist Rachel Carson was not far off the mark in predicting a "silent spring" if the use of hard pesticides remained unregulated. Carson's clarion call appeared years before asbestos, oil spills, PCBs, dioxins, and the cargo of other toxic industrial wastes captured public attention as grave threats to all forms of life.

What we do know is that animals please us. They have their needs and habits, as we have ours, and each of them lives a wondrous life in its own way. Many are stunningly beautiful, graceful, and wonderfully adept at inhabiting what we regard as strange, out-of-the-way places. Others move about in mysterious ways—making migratory journeys that only the finite size of the earth can limit. Most significant, perhaps, animals excite admiration because they are our companions. They swarm over hills and valleys, burrow into the earth, swim rivers and oceans, and liven the air with their calls and songs. Animals infuse the face of nature with that intimacy and difference that poets strive to capture. They come and go with the ticking clock of our years, emphasizing the patterns and cycles of the seasons and bringing reassurance and continuity to our lives. They keep us in touch with our world, perpetually renewing the wonder and awe of childhood.

Biologist and nature philosopher Aldo Leopold once remarked that "for one species to mourn the death of another is a new thing under the sun." He was referring to the extinction of the passenger pigeon, whose huge, overwhelming flocks people called a "biological storm." Certainly this bird would not have mourned our passing as we now lament its own, he said. So why does it sadden us so? Because for one thing we can never, never experience that exultation and excitement that John James Audubon felt when he saw pigeon bands blackening the sky, filling it with thunder. In Texas, birdman George Finlay Simmons noted that in fall 1878 "string after string of many thousands of birds passed over [Austin]; many lit in the tall trees along Barton Creek just above its mouth . . . literally loading down the limbs." We will never see that special bird, never hear the swift, vigorous wingbeats that launched it from season to season, just as we shall never again witness a mile-long smoky plume of Eskimo curlews, their clamor shrill as the wind through the ropes of a full-rigged sailing ship. Today, news of a possible single Eskimo curlew or of a pair brings birders flocking to the west shore of Galveston Island where a relict flight of the shorebirds, mixed in with larger curlews and whimbrels, may yet turn up, as small sickle-billed birds pause on a long passage from Argentina's grasslands to summer nesting grounds somewhere above the Arctic Circle.

To lose such living things, including invertebrates and plants, closes options for both our learning and our enjoyment. It was an issue that gentle outdoorsman Roy Bedichek pondered in his excellent book *Adventures With a Texas Naturalist.* Bedichek disliked traditional Texas bragging about dinosaur tracks or longhorns; he was much more interested in how creatures cooperate with one another, "clubbing together," he called it. He liked to watch, to quietly observe organisms, not with a killer's intent but with an artist's appreciation for how an animal was shaped, what colors it showed, and how it moved and sounded. His warm and often humorous empathy for the wildlife of Texas drew him to the study of the state's nongame animals, an all too rare interest in the years before the environmental movement of the sixties.

Leopold and Bedichek, compatriots writing at the same time, shared a common passion for "seeing" animals. As did Bedichek, Leopold liked to "see" by learning animal ways through patient observation. He learned in the outdoors, sometimes stalking and capturing his prey. "Goose Music," spinning from the autumn wind, stirred in him the instinct to hunt. Bedichek heard the same music funneled on the north wind and pondered its arrival: how did geese get to Texas, where did they stay, how many young did they tend, and what were gaggles of them saying as they beat over central Texas toward the Gulf of Mexico? He included cranes, eagles, mockingbirds, and even factory-raised poultry—"denatured chickens," he called them—in his repertoire of concern, convincing his readers that all those creatures spoke to the soul and were valuable fellow beings in this world.

We should like this book to follow in the footsteps of both men, not to soliloquize or offer profound insights about life or being but rather to talk about animals that add character to landscapes across this enormous state and to encourage people to see them as more than meat or feathers, machines or little people, there simply by our leave and for our pleasure. Animals and plants surround us, they are our fellow voyagers, and some of them require our active assistance if they are to persist. Some shy away when approached, others tolerate human presence or even seek us out. We can turn them into trophies to nail on den walls or to fill 35mm carousel projectors. But we need them even more to fill our experiences with shape and color and sounds, to compose a fuller and more substantial stage for our lives. They are a way of encounter, enabling us to discover more about our bonds to the world we inhabit, and about ourselves.

Many people argue that lowered populations of animals, resulting in fewer species, are the inevitable price we pay for progress. But is that loss our gain, or are we fouling our nest; that is, by reducing biological diversity, are we eliminating those species that act as rivets to make communities of plants and animals and the ecosystems they inhabit function properly? How many rivets can pop loose and be lost before the structural integrity of an airplane, spaceship, or whatever metaphor we employ for the ecosystem, is jeopardized? We may lose a few, we may not notice just how many, but at some point, with continued inattention or neglect, the vehicle may just cease to operate, suddenly and with devastating consequences.

That is how Paul and Anne Ehrlich picture the continued loss of organisms worldwide, an analogy the two Stanford-based biologists draw in their 1981 book, *Extinction.* Organisms are the rivets that sustain life on earth. Some of them fix energy; others provide us with food or act as decomposers to recycle nutrients. Losing one here and another there will not make any measurable difference to life's functions, but as whole families and genera of them disappear, life on "spaceship earth" will become increasingly perilous.

Portents of doom characterize such metaphors. Some biologists argue that appeals on behalf of maximizing species diversity in biological systems have been overstated. For example, Norman Myers, an Oxford-based ecologist, reminds us that although variety may be the spice of life, it is not life's essence. It is wrong to assume that the more species there are in an ecosystem, the more stable that system will be.

An obvious case in point is the world's tropical rain forests, now under siege. That most complex biota is very sensitive to human ingress and alteration.

Like the miner's canary indicating the presence of potentially lethal gas in subterranean workplaces, the bald eagle, peregrine falcon, and even coniferous trees sensitive to the effects of air pollution and acid rain exemplify organisms acting as indicators of the environment's general well-being. But they also represent much more. Rare species such as whales are materially useful for the food and other goods they supply – that is why so many are endangered. They may be spiritually important, too, symbolizing wild nature, the continuity of life, and hope for a future. Some people regard these species quite literally as nature's works of art, to be enjoyed not merely for the sentimental delight we find in having them around as curiosities or companions but also for their intrinsic worth. Animals have their own compelling and mysterious integrity, and more and more people believe we should meet with them on their own terms.

Certainly the bison, pronghorn antelope, and white-tailed deer supplied material benefits to nineteenth-century Texans, so much so that overhunting seriously jeopardized the existence of the game mammals. Meat from those and other species sustained newcomers until domestic stock and crops grew plentiful enough to sustain settlement. Meat and skins were suitable for barter or exchange as well, and toward the end of the century, as expanding railroads opened up vast new markets, hunters decimated entire populations of waterfowl and game mammals. Large grazing mammals also stood in the way of grass-hungry cattle, which ranchers turned loose in ever-increasing numbers.

Those and similar species declined drastically primarily because of direct exploitation, but habitat loss also figured prominently. In the opinion of old-timers, bison consumed forage that God intended for cattle. Settlers shot bison for material gain and out of spiritual zeal – the buffalo represented the old West whereas the ranching of cattle spelled the new, and there was no place for the huge, shaggy, intractable mammal whose herds blanketed the unfenced rangelands. The federal government also worked to kill off bison to destroy the economic base of the Plains Indians and thereby bring them under U.S. control.

In recent decades we have learned much more about such "bad" or "useless" animals and are less cavalier in passing judgments. Today, biologists assure us that rare organisms may provide important genetic materials for the world in the 21st century. We will certainly be calling upon wild plants and animals to offer us new forms of food. Currently fewer than twenty species of food plants furnish upwards of 90 percent of the world's food resources, and we depend on only seven or eight of them – grains and vegetables – for the major portion of our nourishment. With the world population racing toward five billion and possibly doubling that figure within the next forty years, the importance of developing underutilized foodstuffs and conserving the gene pools of wild species and varieties cannot be overstressed.

Margery Oldfield reminds us in her book *The Value of Conserving Genetic Resources* that returns from commonly used crops are dropping off in relation to technological input. Accordingly, she insists that we must "carefully scrutinize the unused potentials of our biotic support systems," including those wild organisms that are threatened and endangered. That is especially significant because just over one in four terrestrial plant species is edible, yet we have used less than 4 percent, or about 3,000 species, and have put only 150 species into commercial cultivation. That narrowing of our plant preferences means that we invest time and energy in genetic improvements in our most productive crops, such as wheat, rice, maize, and potatoes, while neglecting the development of other nutritious foodstuffs.

Oldfield states that within the United States more than 160 wild ancestors of modern crops and 150 others related to forage plant species are threatened with extinction. Such species possess genes that can improve existing plants. Wild teosinte, the weedy progenitor of corn, for example, has reportedly influenced the development of that vital food.

Wild animals are used less commonly than plants to improve domesticated species because in most cases their hybrids are sterile or significantly less fertile. The bison, however, has proved a valuable asset in breeding with cattle (most notably with Brahman and Charolais blood). Wild geese and ducks produce fertile offspring when crossed with domesticated counterparts. Three species threatened in the U.S., the Hawaiian goose, Hawaiian duck, and Laysan duck, show promise for improving domestic species. The first two are well adjusted to terrestrial rather than aquatic environments and copulate effectively on land. They consume less animal protein than other barnyard fowl; the Laysan duck can exist without fresh water. Those traits make them potentially useful, especially if they can be genetically transmitted to meat-producing relatives.

Game ranching is another source of animal protein. Several African animals demonstrate possibilities for domestication, including the springbok, eland, and oryx, ungulates that are run with cattle or formed in herds of their own. "Texotics" include those and similar deer and antelope whose native homes are in Africa, Asia, or Europe, and many of which make attractive trophies. The numbers of those foreign mammals are growing in Texas, upwards of 120,000 in a 1985 report, especially in counties on the Edwards Plateau.

An enormous range of drugs and pharmaceutical and industrial commodities depend on processing plant and animal products. One estimate places the commercial value of plant-derived drugs in the U.S. at about $6 billion per year, and of 76 main pharmaceuticals (painkillers, antibiotics, enzymes, hormones, and others) obtained from higher plants, only a half dozen or so can be synthesized commercially in a cost-effective manner. Likewise, snake venoms are useful painkillers, and alantoin, secreted by blowfly larvae, promotes the healing of deep wounds. The study of animal physiology, in particular the circulatory properties of such long-distance fliers as albatrosses and petrels, can help in cardiology research.

Botanists point out the importance of organic alkaloidal compounds (found in about one quarter of all plant species) such as narcotics, painkillers, cardiac stimulants, and carcinogen inhibitors. They exist in tropical rain forest regions, huge areas of which are being destroyed every year. To date we have screened only about 2 percent of the 350,000 land plant species for useful alkaloids—and we have found many already—so pharmaceutical properties in a wide variety of tropical species are being recognized just as we are clearing them away.

Paul and Anne Ehrlich make the right-to-exist argument the linchpin for preserving organisms. Echoing biologist David Ehrenfeld's pronouncement that living things present "an expression of a continuing historical process of immense antiquity and majesty," they join others in questioning the right to treat animals as objects to be used and abused at will, as well as to push entire species into oblivion.

Along with our rights as ecological dominants goes the responsibility of stewardship for the cohabitation of the earth. The responsible exercise of stewardship must eschew chauvinism and homocentricity. Ehrenfeld argues that pleas for an organism's preservation on the basis of its potential value to humans, be that value economic, medical, scientific, spiritual, or otherwise, continue to reflect an impaired vision of our world, that somehow all other life-forms must prove their worthiness to us in order to exist. Other creatures have a right to exist, as we have the moral responsibility to extend our compassion to the land community. Although some would argue that evolution impels us to reduce and eliminate other species (and eventually ourselves), the more creative and constructive approach is to act thoughtfully and intelligently toward other life-forms, to transcend biological determinism and shape a happier fate for our world.

1 LABELS AND NUMBERS

The Division of Endangered Species and Habitat Conservation, within the U.S. Department of Interior's Fish and Wildlife Service, is charged with monitoring those animal and plant species listed as endangered or threatened with extinction. The label "endangered" is given to an organism on the brink of extinction throughout all or a significant portion of its range. As of December 1988, 31 mammals, 61 birds, 8 reptiles, 5 amphibians, 45 fishes, an additional 52 snails, clams, crustaceans, and insects, plus 149 plants, totaling 351 species, fell into that category in the United States. The U.S. Fish and Wildlife Service's *Endangered Species Technical Bulletin* tallied another 49 animals and plants shared with other countries. Upwards of 870 organisms appear on the box score of endangered species worldwide.

An organism is determined to be threatened when it is likely to become endangered in the foreseeable future. Numerically the trend for threatened species is downward toward endangerment and eventual oblivion. Concern, therefore, centers on preventing further losses and rehabilitating populations. Three mammals, 7 birds, 14 reptiles, 25 fishes, and 33 plants are among 99 species listed as threatened in the United States; 39 additional foreign organisms have also joined the total.

Those statistics demonstrate that a small but growing proportion of fauna and flora is in trouble. But it is a static picture. History provides us with a picture of the dynamics of extinction, suggesting forcefully that the current trend is unprecedented in terms of the tempo and scope of loss and extirpation.

If we argue that present disappearance rates are far ahead of historic rates of species formation—a contrast really between life evolving and replacing itself in geological time (tens of thousands to millions of years) versus extinctions in human time (spanning a score or so of years to a century)—what categories are we applying to organisms? Biologists are unsure about just what a species is, and precise definitions are elusive. If two organisms do not interbreed, even though they may live together and have similar characteristics, we tend to think of them as separate species. Put another way, a species consists of a population of fertile organisms that breed together and are isolated reproductively from individuals in other populations. Offspring from the cross-breeding of two species are often sterile. All species of horses, including the zebras, will interbreed and produce young that are almost always infertile. By mating a male donkey with a female horse, humans ingeniously created a vigorous hybrid—the mule. This most useful but sterile member of the horse family can be traced in Mesopotamian painting to the first millennium B.C. and is possibly older in Egypt's decorative art.

Hawks and owls are both birds of prey, but they are of different orders and do not interbreed, whereas forms that are closely related, such as ducks and geese, may produce interspecific hybrids. For example, mallards and black ducks produce healthy ducklings. Mallards and black ducks are considered separate species because individuals usually select mates of their respective kind, although some ornithologists would prefer to call black ducks "black mallards." Reproduction, then, is not an invariable trait for classifying organisms according to species; taxonomic characters such as size, shape, color, and behavioral traits also figure in the determination of species. Increasingly, biologists are comparing the structure of body proteins to establish genetic relationships.

The reason for using the term "species" is to highlight the numerical abundance of species on the earth. Current estimates vary, especially when one tries to total up insects, mites, marine invertebrates, and the like, but biologists frequently cite the figure 10 million as a useful benchmark. There may be more than 10 million, but so far we have names for fewer than one in five of them. Some species are undoubtedly falling into the abyss of extinction without ever being recognized.

Specific numbers worldwide, however, do exist. Experts tell us that there are 4,100 mammals (most, if not all, have names), 8,600 birds, 6,500 reptiles, 2,600 amphibians, and 20,000 fishes, and higher plants top 250,000. In such global terms, Texas' list of species may not seem large. Only about 6.6 percent of the world's birds are Texans in good standing. But the sum of 566 birds, of which 330 or so have either nested or attempted to breed in Texas, is about 150 species more than in neighboring Louisiana, New Mexico, or Oklahoma (each with approximately 400), and tops Arkansas by 250 species. Texas is by far the most species-rich state in the nation for birds, owing to its geographic location. The state lies on the biological crossroads of North America, linking mid- and high-latitude summering bird migrants with their warm, subtropical wintering grounds. Some true tropical species of whistling ducks, flycatchers, and warblers occur in the Rio Grande Valley and into South Texas on the northernmost edges of their ranges, thereby making the 3,000-acre Santa Ana Wildlife Refuge, for instance, the jewel of the nation's federal refuge system.

The crossroads image also applies to other species (plants, mammals, and reptiles). At 267,339 square miles (second only to Alaska and three times the size of the British Isles, or larger than the United Kingdom, West Germany, Holland, and Denmark together), the sheer size of the state suggests physical and biological diversity.

The state's position in the southwest quadrant of the U.S. and Canada promotes the mingling of different temperature and moisture regimes in which native organisms have evolved. One way of viewing that diversity is in terms of the biotic province, that is, a geographic area with identifiable ecological associations that set it apart from adjacent areas. Texas consists of three major biotic provinces and of others that form crossroads or transition zones between them. Taken together, the entire state can be regarded as a transition zone between desert and aridity-adapted plants and animals in the Trans-Pecos and High Plains, moisture-loving organisms in pinelands from East Texas all the way to the Atlantic coast, and flora and fauna in

South Texas that exist in warmth with generally little moisture. The brush complex on the Rio Grande Plain exemplifies the latter province, extending northward into Texas from the lowlands of northeast Mexico.

Between those major provinces, each with its characteristic plants, mammals, lizards, and snakes, there are zones of linkage often referred to as ecotones. The central Texas oak-hickory woodland and prairie is such an ecotone, linking the conifers in the east with the juniper, oak, and mesquite grassland or savannah in the west. The Edwards Plateau is itself an ecotone between the moister prairies in the east (the central Texas blackland, for example) and shortgrass plains of the true West.

Rivers and bankside vegetation provide routeways for plants and animals to move from one province to another. The general northwest to southeast tilt of the state's drainage network has enabled a good many plants and animals (especially from the moister east) to survive in riparian places in the drier, cooler (and higher) localities farther west.

Although we have probably gained more organisms than we have lost over the past 250 years of European settlement, there is little room for comfort. Gains have been made by adding alien plants and animals in the form of domesticated crops and livestock, or as game animals or for ornamental purposes. The accidental importation of rodents, mollusks, bacteria, and other organisms also fills out the impression of gain. The English or house sparrow, for example, was liberated in Galveston in the late 1860s as a decorative bird, reportedly also useful in controlling insects, but the feisty foreigner proved more than a match for cavity-nesting wrens, martins, and titmice. The eastern bluebird is widely regarded as having declined in Texas and elsewhere because of competition from sparrows and the European starling, another United Kingdom import to the eastern states, which reached Texas in the late thirties, probably breeding by the early forties.

The problem lies in the quality of our native wildlife, not just its quantity. How much more is a bluebird or purple martin worth than an alien house sparrow? One can argue in terms of injurious insects consumed by the former versus grain crops raided by the latter. In any event, the sparrow would not be here except for assistance from humans, who at one time regarded the small brown birds as a sign of progress, like gaslights in the streets.

Conservation in Texas

Our headlong rush to rearrange the abundance and distribution of Texas flora and fauna under the guise of improving the environment has still not abated. It began in the 1700s when Spaniards drove sheep and goats into this distant corner of their empire. The arrival of large numbers of Anglo-American colonists starting in the 1820s accelerated and intensified the transformation. New settlers also carried useful plant and animal additions previously unknown. It continued in the 1880s when "beneficial" species such as the German or common carp were stocked in rivers and lakes as "good brain food" to replace native fish that had declined from overfishing, construction of weirs and dams that disrupted their movements and life cycles, and even the use of explosives to stun them. A century ago it was impossible to get more than lip service paid to so-called game laws. The first official state conservator, the fish commissioner, was known as the carp commissioner because his main interest lay in promoting that foreign food fish. The office of fish commissioner was abolished in 1885, not to be resurrected for another decade (see Appendix 1). The brouhaha over carp-raising diverted attention away from more critical issues: the decline in native species and the loss and impoverishment of their habitats.

Texas lagged behind neighboring states in passing legislation designed to protect native wildlife. Moreover, laws that did pass were unenforceable. In 1895 the Legislature reconstituted the fish commissioner's office, and I. P. Kibbe became the first "fish and oyster commissioner." He served for eleven years and made strenuous efforts to protect a coastal fishery subjected to overfishing and pollution. The early 1900s were difficult for Kibbe and his successors, who knew that there was little they could do in the face of a flagrant disrespect for fish and game laws. For example, many county commissioners exempted their jurisdictions from the provisions of game statutes, so any dwindling fish, mammal, and bird population continued to decline. The myth of superabundance, which portrayed Texas as an unlimited kingdom of wildlife resources, still proved more compelling, it seems, than the realities of impending extinction.

Efforts to protect birds, specifically useful insectivorous ones, did prove successful when the Audubon movement reached Texas in 1899. A ground swell of concern about killing birds for their feathers, considered fashionable adornments for women's hats, had led to the formation of the Audubon Society in 1886. The antiplumage league collaborated with scientific and sportsmens' associations to draft laws aimed at curbing the importation and sale of wild bird feathers (more than 100 North American species were involved, but most millinery came from herons, gulls, terns, shorebirds, and waterfowl). The initiatives of the Audubon Society and of ornithologists resulted in a so-called model law, which separated game from nongame birds and beneficial from injurious species. States in the East and Midwest began to take an active interest in bird protection. Texas passed its own model law in 1903.

The following year the National Audubon Society employed a warden to police a seabird colony on Matagorda Bay. It also defended the 1903 law, which made it illegal to market game animals, against the efforts of hoteliers and restaurant owners to amend it. Audubon representatives in Texas, notably Captain M. B. Davis and Henry P. Attwater, campaigned to educate the public, particularly schoolchildren, about the value of wildlife and forged links with politicians, women's groups, and farm organizations to promote the bird protection cause. By about 1912, state Audubon secretary Davis judged that the bird protection cause was headed for smoother waters. Federal measures for migratory bird species, exemplified by a convention between the U.S. and Canada, resulted in the Migratory Bird Treaty Act (ratified in 1918), which added teeth to efforts aimed at stamping out professional hunting. It established hunting guidelines and prohibited shipment and export of migratory species.

Addition of a game arm to the State Fish and Oyster Commission in 1907 institutionalized interest in the management of important mammals and birds. The Texas State Sportsman's Association endorsed a campaign to outlaw market hunting, and interests coalesced around species such as the mountain sheep and pronghorn antelope that appeared most likely to disappear entirely. Hunting licenses were also mandated; proceeds from their sale went toward hiring game wardens. After 1910, a small cadre of dedicated individuals began to effectively tackle the poaching question and to monitor bag limits and the types of weapons used in hunting. Truly comprehensive enforcement occurred in the mid-twenties when the Legislature turned over the entire game fund from hunting license revenues, and 45 game wardens fanned out across Texas.

Regulations to end or control hunting proved the key to Texas wildlife conservation during the first two decades of the current century. Research into the life histories of game animals and measures to restock them in areas from which they had been extirpated took off after 1925.

Between 1920 and 1940 about 100,000 bobwhite quail, imported mostly from Mexico, were offered to landowners who were interested in restocking rangelands. A reconstituted Game, Fish, and Oyster Commission (made up of a six-member board) helped streamline that kind of conservation. Federal Aid in Wildlife Restoration (commonly called the Pittman-Robertson Act) generated monies from an excise tax on sporting arms and ammunition, allowing white-tailed deer, pronghorn antelope, wild turkey, and other once-abundant animals to be studied, transported, and released to provide seed stock in new areas. The King Ranch and Aransas Wildlife Refuge provided some deer and turkeys for central Texas.

Allied with the desire to resuscitate game populations by preserving, trapping, and transplanting, landowners established a series of game preserves in which they agreed to protect certain species for at least ten years. In its thirties heyday, about 2.7 million acres fell into the game preserve category, becoming reservoirs in which transplanted wildlife could grow.

Efforts for Nongame Wildlife

A third trend in wild animal conservation, beyond game animal protection, management, and rehabilitation, has opened up interest in nongame wildlife and also plants. Concern about the survival of threatened and endangered organisms gathered momentum in the mid-sixties and culminated in federal and state laws that have had lasting implications for the ways we treat Texas biota (see Appendix 2).

The 1966 Endangered Species Preservation Act, subsequently updated and strengthened by further federal backing, has been the key for nongame wildlife conservation throughout the nation. The first 1966 law charged the Secretary of the Interior with drawing up an official list of threatened and endangered species. Its purpose was to scrutinize, assess, and ultimately to preserve the nation's rich endowment of living things. Guidelines for protecting disappearing organisms (or at least ones that we regard as vital or important) rest on the fact that extinction is irrevocable and final—the loss of a unique biological asset. Given the galloping pace and scope of environmental transformation, it was clear then, and remains clear now, that many plants and animals cannot sustain pressures from hunting, disturbance, or habitat loss. Benefits from the survival of wildlife have not usually been factored into decisions made in the public or private sector. Legislation for threatened species goes beyond the special needs of interest groups, such as sportsmen's groups, to regard the whole fabric of life and the mechanisms that support life's durability as being essential to society.

Information about species in trouble has doubled and tripled in the last few years, and so has the knowledge and expertise that goes into plans for their recovery. It is, however, extremely difficult to measure the effectiveness of policies like the Endangered Species Act. Successes may be due to a variety of factors, many of which are independent of federal conservation efforts. The interactions of human society and culture with the ecology and biology of millions of diverse creatures are overwhelmingly complex, and even seemingly straightforward questions as to whether prospects for this or that species are improving or deteriorating are difficult to answer. In the face of such uncertainty, officialdom is readily criticized.

Conservation critics of the U.S. Fish and Wildlife Service's program remain impatient about the rate at which organisms receive attention. In the twelve-year period after the 1973 act, the official list grew by 429 species, averaging 35 per year. There is, however, a sizable backlog—more than 1,000 additional species are worthy of inclusion. At present rates, it will take more than a quarter of a century to clear that backlog, by which time many plants and animals will have passed over the brink into oblivion. The subspecies of Henslow's sparrow in Texas, for example, recently became extinct as authorities were debating its proposed listing.

Critics demand more money for the program. Although Fish and Wildlife's appropriations have grown sevenfold from 1974 to 1988 ($4.6 million to $31 million), Natural Resources Defense Council researcher Faith Campbell points out that gains in the seventies were not matched in the eighties. Funding in terms of constant dollars stagnated during the Reagan presidency, even though more than 230 species were listed.

A doubling of recent annual appropriations to about $50 million per year would go a long way, according to some, toward dealing with the resulting backlog of candidates for listing and would also provide sufficient funds for states that have entered into cooperative agreements with the federal government to make them equal partners rather than weak sisters in solving problems within their own boundaries.

In May 1988, Texas signed a cooperative agreement with the U.S. Fish and Wildlife Service (made possible under the 1973 law). State officials had tended to regard such agreements as limiting to the state's own plans. However, initial projects to receive the new form of funding have included red-cockaded woodpecker sites and a program for endangered plants. The state clearly recognizes its responsibilities toward endangered species.

In 1970, the Wildlife Division of the Texas Parks and Wildlife Department initiated a nongame program to manage vertebrates not usually hunted, trapped, or fished. The Endangered Species Act, which the 63rd Texas Legislature passed in 1973, added legal clout to the nongame program by providing money for research into endangered species. Under the provisions of Chapter 68 of the Texas Parks and Wildlife Code, the director is instructed to file with the Secretary of State a list of fish and wildlife threatened with statewide extinction. In 1981, a list of endangered plants was also drawn up according to provisions of Chapter 88 of the Parks and Wildlife Code.

In practice, that list has included all of the species in Texas that appear on the federal list of threatened or endangered species, plus additional ones that state authorities believe require inclusion (see Appendix 3). The list is modified periodically as surveys and research uncover information about the life histories, distribution, and population trends of listed organisms.

Surveys have gathered data on such nongame and endangered species as the bald eagle, peregrine falcon, and red-cockaded woodpecker; various articles about those and other species appear regularly in publications and include a bulletin on the life history of the golden-cheeked warbler. The objective is to generate and disseminate knowledge about the species and to establish management practices, including the retention of habitat.

In 1985, a venture aimed at increasing monies in Texas' efforts for nongame and endangered species resulted in a nongame stamp, which raised $350,000. Patterned on a requirement for waterfowl hunters to buy both a federal and a state duck stamp, the nongame stamp (with decal and artwork portraying a pair of whooping cranes) enabled the public to express in a practical way its concern for conservation in Texas. In 1986, Attwater's prairie chicken was featured, followed by the bald eagle in 1987 and the American kestrel in 1988.

The Texas Nongame and Endangered Species Conservation Fund, established by the 68th Legislature, received contributions in 1986 from the sale of the second nongame stamp and print, this time of Attwater's greater prairie chicken. In a new way, nonconsumptive users of wildlife, such as active photographers and bird-watchers, are giving tangible input for ongoing research into nongame and endangered biota.

2 HUMAN EXPLOITATION AND HABITAT CHANGE

With the benefit of hindsight, it is easy and convenient for us to condemn early Texans for exploiting native wildlife. We can draw up a list of mammals and birds that succumbed to improved firearms in the 1800s. Some of them (see Appendix 4) were extirpated by unregulated hunting and trapping, while others faded away as settlers claimed their habitats for crops and introduced livestock as competitors. A dozen or more mammals and birds have vanished, and except for the mountain, or bighorn, sheep, which has been reintroduced from out of state, most have gone for good. It is unclear whether some species were ever common or widely distributed. There is only one detailed record of the grizzly bear; it comes from the Davis Mountains in 1890, when stockmen killed an old male for preying on livestock. Probably other grizzlies inhabited the Guadalupe Mountains. The sharp-tailed grouse inhabited only the extreme northwest Panhandle (Dallam County), and although it was reportedly quite common in the 1800s, it disappeared about 1900.

Experts do not agree whether Merriam's elk, *Cervus elaphus*, represented a full species or subspecies of the more common American elk. Merriam's elk, the largest of the deer family in Texas, reportedly ranged from the southern Guadalupe Mountains northward into New Mexico but vanished before 1900. If we accept it as a subspecies of the American elk, or wapiti (which was imported into Texas from North Dakota in 1928), then it belongs in the same category as the extirpated race of the wild turkey of east Texas and the greater prairie chicken of the central blacklands. The latter bird's sole representative in Texas is the currently endangered Attwater's prairie chicken.

There is also the issue of localized or absolute extinction. The greater prairie chicken has been extirpated from the prairies of central Texas but is holding its own in the U.S. Midwest, although the Attwater's race is in severe trouble on the Gulf Coast prairie. Nobody is likely to see the ivory-billed woodpecker again in the Big Thicket or in any other remote woodland in the American South. Nor will anyone ever discover an active roost of passenger pigeons. The pigeon and the Carolina parakeet no longer exist; they are extinct. A subspecies of the ivory-bill still survives in Cuba, but its American mainland counterpart probably lives no more. Bison and wolves still survive. In Texas, however, the big, shaggy bison exists as a captive on ranches, and to see a wild gray (timber) wolf, one must head for the forests of northern Minnesota. The old Texas loafer, or lobo, is gone forever.

As we look at the list, we can indict our forebears for the narrowness of their vision and their selfish zeal in fulfilling immediate, material, and personal needs, which appear to have conflicted with most of the animals in question. It is important, however, to see ourselves on the Texas frontier 150 years ago and to understand two facts of pioneer life. First, wild plants and animals offered the necessary and sole means for survival—settlers regarded wildlife as plentiful enough to always sustain them. Many people lived entirely off the land. They hunted deer, black bear, wild turkey, and similar edible creatures. They "lined" wild honey bees back to their tree homes and collected fruits, nuts, and roots. In their view, animals existed to satisfy human needs by providing meat for the larder, horns for buttons and pegs, fat for cooking and candles, hides for clothing and furniture, feathers for bedding, and bones and sinew for ornaments and threads. Wild animal products were, quite simply, vital to frontier life.

Settlers bagged various species with ease and in sufficient numbers until they had cleared their lands for crops and were able to insure that the few oxen, milch cows, and hogs that they had brought into the wilderness prospered and multiplied. They also exploited native species out of tradition; it was a part of becoming established in a new place. And people loved to spin yarns about hunting prowess. They recounted ways of stalking and bagging wild game; they discussed the behaviors of different animals, quirks, idiosyncracies, the times of the day or season when a quarry was most vulnerable, and the localities in which it might be most easily taken. Men shared opinions about the best methods of hunting and the number, type, and reliability of weapons and dogs that could bring the optimal rewards. Dog-talk was a passion, and they lavished great attention and affection on hounds in raising and training them to hunt.

Second, it is important to realize just how plentiful—superabundant by modern standards—wild animals actually were. Wealthy sportsmen made special trips to Texas to bag favorite trophies. The bison, symbol of the wild West, was an especially favored target, and even as that lumbering giant was being brought numerically to its knees by the 1870s, the Gulf plain continued to beckon other nimrods who regarded its bays and estuaries as a winter paradise with an assortment of waterbirds that teemed in the marshes and lagoons. If Texas was a sportsman's dream, its prolific wildlife provided both market hunters and plume men with a profitable livelihood. Blasting into flocks of mammals and birds, sometimes even at night, those operators supplied urban markets with fresh meat and later sent produce to distant cities when refrigeration and railroad links came in.

By the turn of the present century, many hunters knew that native wildlife populations had plummeted and, indeed, that several species were doomed to extinction. Yet the size of the state and the right of Texans to bear arms helped continue exploitation. Overhunting may have jeopardized game populations in settled places (in the rolling prairies between the Gulf lowland and desert west, for example), but, people argued, the same or similar animals existed outside cultivated areas. Various species could replenish their numbers in other places—the frontier was, after all, generous space.

Space was limitless; so were good soils, fine pasture grasses, water, timber, and huntable wildlife. Those resources beckoned hardier souls to make the long journey from the East, even from Europe. Concerns about exploitation were never a factor in settlers' ideas. Their duty was to tame the wilderness by building homes and clearing land. Wild animals entered into the process by furnishing the actual means to accomplish the task of settlement; they also provided the context for a growing solidarity that turned newcomers into Texans. In hunting, menfolk in particular honed woodcraft skills. They also learned Texas geography and details of the countryside while competing to determine who could kill that extra-big buck or shoot it at the farthest distance. Settlers took pleasure in outdoor pursuits, and the chase and possession of native game educated them about each other and about their new home.

For half a century after Texas declared independence from Mexico (in 1836), people were more concerned with making "improvements" than with gauging the ill effects that clearance and settlement was having upon indigenous biota. The impetus was in working to make the republic, and later the state of Texas, grow as an economic emporium. That meant sowing and cropping in the east, running cattle, sheep, and goats in the west, and subduing the wilderness everywhere, ridding the landscape of that solitary, unpeopled look. In short, Texas was fashioned in the image of other places; the difference lay in its overwhelming size and in the quality and variety of its natural resources. Anything and anyone who presented an obstacle to the exploitation of those resources was subjugated. In respect to specific animal species, the prevailing attitude doomed the buffalo, or bison, a huge and intractable wild bovine that competed with domestic stock for fodder. The bison, like the Indian, was a symbol of the Old West, a raw and unsullied America. As such, it was an anachronism, something that stood in the way of progress and the march of modern life.

The bison, like other mammals, was free — a resource whose exploitation came cheap and easy. When hunting weapons became more effective, inroads into the populous herds in the unexplored west, or so-called mountain zone of Texas, were more substantial and proved detrimental to the beast's survival.

The state was full of similarly free goods. The passenger pigeon abounded in the woodlands of east and central Texas during winter months. Being highly gregarious and roosting in enormous flocks numbering into the millions, it was a natural target for professional and amateur hunters. The same was true for marine turtles along the middle and lower Gulf Coast. That Texas Fishery burgeoned late, but in the 1880s and 1890s, both inshore and vessel catches grew substantially. The principal target was the large sea turtle population that inhabited shallow lagoons and bays during summer and fall. Between 1880 and 1895, several million pounds of sea turtle came out of Matagorda Bay and Aransas Bay into canneries near Rockport and at Indianola. The Laguna Madre also supplied sea turtles to processing plants in Corpus Christi and Port Isabel. Like the bison and the wild pigeon, turtles gave out quickly.

The story has been much the same for the black bear (*Ursus americanus*). Anglo settlers knew the familiar bruin from back East. They used bear oil for cooking and lamps; also, as settlements proliferated, native Indians made a handy profit selling bear oil to newcomers. Bears were also a menace to the pigs that early Texas farmers loosed to forage in the woods. Killing the lumbering beasts thus became a necessity, but it was also great fun. Bear hunts in east Texas are legendary; "the greatest sport on earth," declared Carter Hart, one of its last practitioners, whose recollections are recorded in *Big Thicket Legacy*, edited by Campbell and Lynn Loughmiller (1977). Clearing out bears soon decimated the population. By 1900, bear hunts existed only in the memories of old-timers who told of how things used to be. Bears roamed the more remote areas of the Pineywoods and southern Edwards Plateau for a few more years, but today they are gone. Odd animals may exist in the mountains of the Trans-Pecos, but the species essentially has been extirpated from the state. Although black bears remain in relatively high numbers in other places nationwide, there are no plans at present to bring them back to the Lone Star state.

Other animals, the canids and larger members of the cat family, also required purposeful elimination. In the minds of townspeople and ranchers alike, wolves, cougars, bobcats, and jaguars had no redeeming value other than as decorative skins and trophies to brag about. Prairie dogs were obstacles like bison—their burrows could cause a horse to throw a rider or break a fetlock, and they competed, just as did bison, for precious grass. In that way, predators, and rodents like prairie dogs and jackrabbits, were just bad and nasty.

Too Big: *The Bison*

The cowlike bison (*Bison bison*), with its characteristic shoulder hump and thick, shaggy hair over its head, neck, and shoulders, once roamed much of Texas. The huge beasts, weighing as much as

2,000 pounds, occupied eastern counties (except the impenetrable Big Thicket), ranging into the coastal prairie and westward to the Pecos River. Debate centers around whether the bison inhabited the drier plateaus and mountains beyond the Pecos River. David J. Schmidly's *The Mammals of Trans-Pecos Texas* notes its "undoubted" existence in the Big Bend and the Guadalupe Mountains; however, animals may have been scattered by a general lack of water or insect pests. By about 1850, hunters had cleared out those so-called buffalo, although longtime resident Judge Oscar W. Williams remembered a few head mixed in with cattle near Horse Head Crossing on the Pecos River as late as 1895. The Pecos River's steep, incised banks were an obstacle to such large mammals, and Williams believed they were never common west of the river. Numbers increased beyond a north-south line drawn some 100 miles east of the Pecos, and northward along the headwaters of the Red, Brazos, and Colorado rivers.

Whatever its aboriginal range and numbers (estimates run as high as 60 million nationwide), the bison fell prey to hunters. People shot it for robes, and stockmen disliked its appetite for grass intended, in their opinion, for cattle and other livestock. Colonel Charles Goodnight reportedly drove 10,000 bison out of Palo Duro Canyon in 1876 when he claimed it for his ranch.

The story of the bison's demise is a sad one. Goodnight, famous for the herd he conserved in Texas, was saddened by the passing of this monarch of the plains or, more specifically, by the callous and perfunctory way "sportsmen" shot into herds thronging close to newly laid railroad tracks. He concluded that "the buffalo had to go, of course, but there was no excuse for the hurry, waste and savagery that attended their extermination."

In the early 1850s, one explorer along the Red River, Captain Randolph B. Marcy, noted that the animals' range had contracted markedly as thousands were felled for their skins and sometimes only for their tongues, which hunters cut out as symbols of prowess. About a decade earlier other commentators noted the bison's disappearance from the settled areas of central and coastal Texas.

It took approximately fifty years to finish off this species; activities around Fort Griffin, Shackelford County, in the 1870s proved most decisive. In 1874, the Moar brothers, armed with Sharps rifles that could drop a bull bison at 600 yards, a lively demand for hides from tanners in the East, and experience from hunting the shaggy beasts on Kansas rangelands, headed for the Texas Panhandle. Within months Fort Griffin became the base for their activities, and other buffalo hunters joined them in the systematic culling of the last sizable segment of America's southern herd.

Reportedly, Wright Moar used to ride out with wagons and a posse of skinners, or strippers, and select a group of bison that he knew had recently fed and was, therefore, less likely to stampede. Dismounting, he crawled to within about 200 yards of the loafing animals, aimed for the lead bison's lungs, and blasted. When that animal collapsed, he methodically shot another, then another, making up a stand of twenty or forty, perhaps even a hundred, which he shot down in late morning. The strippers would then move in to butcher the carcasses so that the skins and choice meat could be hauled away to Fort Griffin.

The enormous piles of dried hides around shipping points and the vast boneyards strewn across the plains reflected the extent of buffalo slaughter practiced by hundreds of professional men. By 1879, the hunters had completed their extirpation; mopping up took another five or six years. Biologist Vernon Bailey supplied the final details: "Landlord Holman of the Monahans Hotel [Monahans, Texas], who is an old-timer here, informs me that the last buffalo in the sand-hill region was killed in the winter of 1885 by a professional hunter, George Cansey, who is credited with having killed more buffalo than any other man in Texas." That last episode involved a cow and calf near Midland. Cansey shot the female and roped the calf, which C. C. Slaughter of Fort Worth eventually barbecued at a social gathering—a true Texas finale, but a sad commentary on man's encounter with nature.

TOO POPULOUS: *The Passenger Pigeon*

The passenger pigeon (*Ectopistes migratorius*), like the bison, attracted wide attention because it was enormously abundant and gregarious, feeding, nesting, and roosting in huge flocks. The "wild pigeon," as people named it, thundered across eastern North America, often arriving unexpectedly to feast on nuts, berries, and acorns, then moving off again as suddenly as it had come, filling the horizons and darkening the skies with masses of speeding birds.

Major concentrations of those fleet members of the dove family (*Columbidae*) existed in the East and Midwest. The passenger pigeon resembled the smaller mourning dove but was bluer on the upper parts and redder below. Wintering birds visited the southern hardwood forests from east Texas to the Carolinas and Florida before returning north each spring. East and northeast Texas was included in the pigeon's aboriginal range. People in those counties awaited the great flights during October and November when birds arrived to seek out acorns, earthworms, and other dainties. In some years, the wild pigeons pushed westward into the Hill Country and Edwards Plateau or southward to the Gulf—a great invasion occurred in Houston in October 1873. Precise routes changed according to the availability and abundance of mast, or tree-yielding foods, but grain crops were also subjected to attack, which earned the pigeon a reputation as a pest.

Harry Oberholser's splendid book *The Bird Life of Texas* (Vol. 1, pp. 415–422) offers firsthand accounts of the pigeon's appearance in oak country and its habit of roosting in flocks running into the millions of birds.

One famous roost along Coon Creek, near Athens, Henderson County, consisted of a 25-square-mile rolling area of oak woodland. Tree cover provided security for wild pigeons from at least 1865 through 1893, when the birds petered out. According to Oberholser, residents remembered how pigeons shattered tree limbs by the weight of their numbers, how they fanned out at daylight to feed, then streamed back to the oaks and alders each evening about an hour before sunset. Oberholser estimated that 15 million birds wintered along Coon Creek.

Such lively spectacles attracted the attention of settlers, some of whom feared that pigeons were pilfering crops and wild foods useful for hogs. Texans banded together to club, shoot, and stupefy birds by burning sulfurous fumes beneath their roosts. They bagged enough birds to feed entire communities and loosed their hogs to gobble up decaying remains. Commercial hunters also took advantage of the pigeon's gregarious ways and killed large numbers.

Ultimately, that human predation brought about the demise of the passenger pigeon. Its extirpation is more poignant considering that its numbers were once so large they were often impossible to estimate (Oberholser mentions five *billion* for North America). The last known pigeon, Martha, died in the Cincinnati Zoo on September 1, 1914; the big flights in Texas had ended years earlier, the winter of

1881–82 being the last memorable one, when people reported them over Austin in Travis County and also in Harris and Real counties.

The passenger pigeon is dead. An exciting roar and chatter from communal places added vibrancy to the frontier. It was part of the winter experience.

TOO EDIBLE: *Sea Turtles*

Five species of marine turtles inhabit warm waters of the Texas Gulf Coast. Two of them, the hawksbill—the famous tortoise-shell-producing turtle—and gigantic leatherback, occur infrequently, but others such as the green turtle and loggerhead were once common and still persist, though in enormously reduced numbers. All sea turtles are listed or are likely to be listed as endangered species. By congregating on sandy beaches where they scoop out nests, they became susceptible to predators, particularly humans who slaughter the creatures for their shells, skins, and meat and pilfer their eggs.

The green sea turtle (*Chelonia mydas*) supported a sizable bay fishery in Texas during the final thirty years or so of the nineteenth century. Fishermen snagged the large reptiles, accustomed to grazing sea grasses, with seines and special nets deployed to enmesh a turtle's head or flipper as it passed through shallow channels. Men operated turtle nets from Galveston Bay southward, and in their heyday they landed more than half a million pounds of green turtle annually. So abundant was turtle meat that some beef packing plants turned to canning turtles for soup; others canned fish and turtles. Such factories operated in Indianola (before it was flattened by the 1886 hurricane), in Fulton near Rockport, in Corpus Christi, and in Port Isabel.

Aransas Bay, north of Corpus Christi, was the center of the turtle industry, and its cannery outlet was in Fulton. In 1890, more than 470,000 pounds of green turtle, valued at $7,857, came from 155 special nets set in Aransas Bay.

Captured green turtles were a windfall for coastal fishermen. The marine creatures were important during summer and early autumn and could be kept alive in pens, or crawls, staked out in shallow water. Turtle men used to send some to New Orleans trussed on the decks of Morgan steamships, which connected the coastal towns to Galveston and New Orleans. Turtles fetched between 1 cent and 3 cents a pound, so a large animal was worth perhaps $3 or $4. In the spring, the same fishermen turned to plume hunting, shooting into colonies of herons and seabirds, as another sideline to bay and open sea fishing.

Once the canneries were established and turtling became organized, the industry peaked quickly, then collapsed. In 1890, the weight of turtles landed exceeded Florida's, the traditional center of the U.S. industry, but it did not last. Overfishing quickly decimated turtle numbers, and harvesting restrictions came too late. An 1895 law required licenses for catching turtles and terrapins – and was unenforceable. By 1900, the industry was virtually finished. At that time, the Fulton cannery processed only 20,000 pounds of meat, less than 5 percent of its 1890 total, and soon closed its doors. At the same time, Florida's turtle fishery was valued at more than eight times that of Texas, which composed merely one fifth of the entire Gulf-states turtle industry, after having been dominant a decade earlier.

Today, long-term conservation of sea turtles in Texas is limited. Green turtles are listed as endangered, and a recovery plan was completed in 1984. Yet they, as well as the threatened loggerhead, Kemp's Ridley, and others, continue to be incidentally trapped in shrimp nets at the rate of nearly 48,000 turtles a year nationwide, resulting in an estimated 11,000 deaths. To reduce those numbers, the National Marine Fisheries Service of the U.S. Department of Commerce (which drew up the recovery plan for sea turtles) began a research program in 1978 to develop a device that could be installed in shrimp nets and keep turtles out while still letting in shrimp. In the early eighties the fisheries service in cooperation with shrimp industry representatives and conservationists initiated a voluntary program to encourage the use of turtle excluder devices. After the voluntary program failed to achieve the desired results, the service issued regulations in June 1987 requiring the use of the devices in certain areas and at certain seasons and, where the devices were not mandatory, limiting the tow times of shrimp trawls. That same year the Mexican government also began requiring that the devices be used within its section of the Gulf of Mexico and, unlike the American law, offered no exemptions.

Another recent initiative concerns the most endangered sea turtle in the world, the small Atlantic, or Kemp's Ridley (*Lepidochelys kempi*), which makes synchronized daylight landings in a 17-mile section of beach along the shores of Tamaulipas, about 250 miles south of Brownsville. The turtle is relatively uncommon in Texas, although people have planted its eggs on Padre Island beaches, and in April 1988 a lone female came ashore on Mustang Island a few miles south of Port Aransas and laid 103 eggs. On June 26, under the watchful eyes of turtle experts, 95 baby turtles scrambled into the Gulf surf, progeny of that first documented nesting in a quarter of a century. Only 1 percent of eggs laid by the species are reported to reach adulthood. Worried that the low survival rate, in conjunction with human-created problems, will soon lead to the turtle's extinction, biologists and conservationists began a head-start program for Kemp's Ridleys. Since 1978, about 2,000 eggs have been collected annually in Mexico, hatched on South Padre Island, raised in a federal laboratory in Galveston, then released into the Gulf. Other young turtles found stranded on Gulf beaches are also returned to the sea after being nursed back to health. Anthony Amos, an oceanographer based in Port Aransas and one of the turtle guardians, has discovered that sea turtles may ingest debris, including plastic, that is discarded from oil platforms and oceangoing vessels. Such indigestible products often cause them to die a slow, painful death.

JUST VARMINTS: *Prairie Dogs and the Black-Footed Ferret*

Earlier this century, federally sponsored research into the economic significance of various mammals and birds turned up evidence damning prairie dogs. Using the same argument that had felled the bison, stockmen argued that black-tailed prairie dogs (*Cynomys ludovicianus*) ate too much grass, especially in West Texas, where one single colony stretching from San Angelo to Clarendon reportedly contained about 400 million of the brown, thick-bodied, short-tailed rodents. Biologists calculated that 32 prairie dogs consumed as much as one sheep, and 256 of them as much as a cow or steer. In Texas, the ground-dwelling squirrels ingested enough forage to support 1.5 million cattle. Armed with such statistics, stockmen declared war on the prairie dog.

It was relatively simple. Like wild pigeons, prairie dogs are highly sociable, given to tunneling out a network of warrens beneath grass-filled plains. They establish territories by loud yips and barks and feed around selected burrows. Ranchers and county leaders joined with state and federal authorities to systematically poison sprawling prairie-dog towns which extended from the Edwards Plateau northward through much of the Panhandle and west through the Trans-

Black-Footed Ferret

Pecos to New Mexico. They also exterminated other grassland denizens such as pocket gophers and jackrabbits and killed off coyotes and rattlesnakes as well.

The battle to clear the plains of varmints was won quickly. Field reports filed with the Bureau of Biological Survey after 1915 demonstrate just how effective operations were against prairie dogs. One method was to place grain laced with strychnine in dog towns; for jackrabbits, poisoned pens were built—wired-off squares baited with poisoned alfalfa or maize. In 1922 alone, more than one million acres of the Texas Panhandle were treated, killing off 90 percent or more of prairie dog inhabitants. By 1935, the dog problem was solved. That year's report noted: "the last extensive dog town in the Plains Area passed out of the picture."

Currently, the black-tailed prairie dog is not a threatened species in Texas, as it still persists in greatly reduced numbers in west Texas.

But this grass-loving rodent retains the label of pest (two of its close relatives, the Utah prairie dog and Mexican prairie dog, are endangered but do not occur in Texas). As in many wars, however, the battle to destroy the dog towns also brought ruin to innocent civilians, in this case the secretive and primarily nocturnal black-footed ferret (*Mustela nigripes*), archpredator of prairie dogs. The black-footed ferret is a tan-colored, weasellike carnivore with a black mask and a short tail. Described by John James Audubon and John Bachman in 1851, it occupied dog towns from Alberta and Saskatchewan, Canada, through the open plains south to Texas, New Mexico, and Arizona. As prairie dogs declined, the ferret, which is dependent on them, also vanished. By the late 1970s, experts judged it to be the rarest mammal in North America.

In the last decade or so, a great deal of new information has been gathered about the black-footed ferret. A 1981 questionnaire about the animal's presence turned up 228 reports (including 59 confirmed sightings) of the ferret nationwide; two of the probable listings were for Texas. Both sightings were from near Stratford in Sherman County in the extreme north of the Panhandle in the early seventies. A Texas Parks and Wildlife literature search discovered 18 historic reports of ferrets in Texas, the oldest going back to 1882 from Taylor County and the most recent (1970s) from Dallam and Ochiltree counties in the northern Panhandle. Field surveys have not turned up any ferrets.

In January 1985, the black-footed ferret was a confirmed resident of South Dakota, Utah, and Wyoming. Research into a sizable colony of the ferrets in the Meeteetse area of Park County, Wyoming, confirmed 12 litters in 1982, 18 litters in 1983, and 25 litters in 1984. At least 129 of the mammals were alive in Park County. In little more than a year, an outbreak of sylvatic plague among their prairie-dog prey and canine distemper among ferrets caused a crash in Wyoming. In Fall 1985, six ferrets from the stricken Meeteetse population were captured; all died from distemper. Another six (half of the remainder known in the wild), each isolated from another, were trapped and survived; they have served in a last-ditch effort to breed ferrets in captivity. In 1987, that captive breeding program, based in Sybille, near Wheatland, Wyoming, resulted in the birth of seven kits, bringing the total to 25 ferrets. Forty-four were born in 1988, when plans were formulated to set up other captive breeding centers. In October, seven captive-born ferrets were airlifted to the U.S. National Zoo's research establishment at Front Royal, Virginia, and eight more were destined for the Henry Doorly Zoo in Omaha, Nebraska.

By March 1988, no ferrets were known to be living outside captivity. Federal and state authorities have worked hard to find prairie-dog towns as reintroduction sites and are encouraging people to report sightings of ferrets in the wild. Their objective is to transplant ferrets born in Front Royal and other captive rearing centers into appropriate habitat, they hope as early as 1991, to establish at least ten widely distributed populations. By the early nineties, they hope to have reached 200 breeding pairs or 500 total animals.

JUST BAD: *The Gray Wolf*

In *Cattle Brands*, published in 1906, onetime cowboy and writer Andy Adams offers a vivid account of a wolf drive along the banks of the Cimarron River in present-day Oklahoma. Six hundred horsemen from various cattle camps gathered one Christmas morning to track down and destroy a pack of wolves that had denned up in bankside thickets. In seventeen action-filled pages, Adams conveys the suspense, excitement, and wild confusion of a wolf roundup. In the ensuing melee, cowmen shoot at each other; some are unhorsed and trampled as they converge on cornered wolves. They shoot animals, club some, maim others, roping and dragging them to their deaths. The exciting narrative reveals a lust for wolf blood. It is tacitly understood that no stock killers must be allowed to survive. Nonetheless, a few manage to escape. They are the lucky ones. Wolf carcasses are mute testimony to a confident and unbridled desire to refashion the plains environment and make it safe for human occupation and enterprise.

Such skirmishes in the war against the gray wolf (*Canis lupus*) occurred over and over again on the American prairies and plains, including west Texas. J. Evetts Haley's *The XIT Ranch of Texas* describes how cowhands turned to wolfing in mid-winter when work with cattle was slow. They hunted across a nation of land down the western flank of Texas' Panhandle, chasing the predators for the $10 bounty offered for every lobo, or loafer, as they called the big plains wolves. Some could earn more money in three or four months of bounty work than during the remainder of the year. They tracked wolves along the rough edges of valleys or escarpments like the Caprock, cutting off individuals from their well-hidden dens. A gorged wolf returning in the early morning from a successful hunt was no match for a smart cow pony, which could run the canid down in a mile or two, allowing the rider to rope or simply shoot the fatigued beast in the end. Inexperienced wolfers, however, could break down a horse if they followed an agile wolf too hard across the vast plain. The technique was to lope after it, wearing the varmint down until it slowed after many miles.

The practice of chasing wolves on horseback was complemented by the use of hounds to track them to their dens. In spring, XIT men would crawl into those breeding cavities, shoot the females by shining a candle to spot their eyes, and drag out the pups. In 1896, one man reportedly destroyed 84 lobos in that way.

Domesticated livestock and wolves are considered incompatible. The policy of extirpating the wolf goes back to the 1600s, when bounties insured that the carnivores were destroyed in the American colonies. In the succeeding centuries, killing for economic reasons and for sport has reduced the timber, or gray, wolf to an endangered species. Formerly the animals ranged throughout most of North America's heartland from Alaska (where they remain widely distributed) to Central Mexico. Today, south of the Canadian border, *Canis lupus* has a limited range in Michigan, Minnesota, Montana, Idaho, and Mexico's states of Chihuahua and Durango (where fewer than fifty so-called Mexican wolves, *Canis lupus baileyi*, existed in 1980).

One reason we have persecuted this intelligent carnivore so intensely is our fear that the wolf will turn its proverbial cunning on us. Folklore has transmogrified the sociable and gregarious mammal into an implacable, savage killer as capable of chasing down or ambushing humans as it is the deer, birds, jackrabbits, and smaller rodents off which it regularly feeds.

Given the deep anxiety and clear documentation of the wolf as a habitual stock killer, the federal Bureau of Biological Survey (later the U.S. Fish and Wildlife Service) established a predator control program in 1915. It made immediate, substantial, and long-term inroads into populations in west Texas. Numbers of the doglike carnivore, which superficially resembles a large German shepherd with color variations from white through black, roamed the Panhandle, the Trans-Pecos, the Rolling Plains, and western areas of the Edwards Plateau. In 1907, federal biologist Vernon Bailey reported that the big wolves were "still abundant and very destructive to stock" from such widely separated places as Henrietta (near Wichita Falls), Amarillo, Fort Stockton, and San Angelo. In 1921, however, after five years of coordinated efforts aimed at trapping and poisoning, predator control expert Cedric Landon announced that "grey wolves are practically extinct in Texas." In the half century after federal intervention began, more than 34,000 wolves (mostly red wolf and red wolf–coyote crosses) were killed in Texas; the lobo does not appear in statistics after about 1926.

Reports turn up from time to time in the Trans-Pecos as individual lone wolves have strayed into Texas from northern Mexico. Occasionally, reports come from the mountains of Wyoming and Arizona, but for all intents and purposes the gray wolf is extinct in the Southwest. In Texas, its fate was sealed when Andy Adams was writing.

JUST NASTY: *The Jaguar*

Naturalist Alfred Russel Wallace called the jaguar (*Felis onca*) "the most powerful and dangerous animal inhabiting the American continent." Wallace encountered this cat in the heart of its range, along the banks of Brazil's Rio Negro, but the jaguar once roamed as far north as Texas, New Mexico, Arizona, southern California, and perhaps even into Louisiana. Sam Houston reported to John James Audubon and John Bachman, who were preparing their book on American mammals, that he had had several encounters with jaguars east of the San Jacinto River, and they occurred, he noted, "abundantly on some of the Rio Grande's tributaries." The big feline found excellent cover in dense thickets in the lower Rio Grande Valley and east Texas where it could prey on deer and a variety of small game.

Although Wallace expressed awe and admiration for the jaguar, a naturalist's eye can hardly be expected of those trying to settle and make a living off the land. *Felis onca* is the largest of American wildcats; adult males may weigh 200 pounds or more and grow to lengths in excess of six feet. Unlike the bear or red wolf, *el tigre*, as it is also called, has no tendency to shyness, and the livestock that farmers and ranchers depended upon made easy meals. The fate of such a large, ferocious, and beautifully pelaged carnivore padding through moist lowland swamps and forests—prime agricultural lands—and mauling horses, mules, and cattle could have been easily predicted. Probably never as abundant as Houston described, the jaguar was uncommon by the late nineteenth century, and there are only four reports from Texas after 1905. The big cat was hunted out and exploited for its pelt. A few loners may cross the border from time to time, but the species essentially has disappeared from Texas; the last reports were in the late forties from Kleberg and Cameron counties.

Biologist Frederick R. Gehlbach notes that unlike the cougar, the jaguar is a habitat specialist, preferring the same well-watered lowlands prized for crops. It cannot retreat to isolated mountains or be ecologically flexible in other ways. Its life-style collided head-on with that of man, and archpredator man won. Undoubtedly many would argue that the extirpation of the jaguar, wolf, and black bear was greatly to our credit, and there is logical justification for that position. But what of lesser obstacles, such as the passenger pigeon, mountain sheep, black-footed ferret, and ivory-billed woodpecker? In their accounts, many settlers express awe and excitement in taming the wild land, but they didn't despise all predators. For earlier generations, the experience of wild animals was a given; the thundering flights of passenger pigeons, the massive herds of buffalo, the stealth and ferocity of wolves and jaguars, all riveted human inhabitants to the landscape, drew them in and helped to make them knowledgeable and at home in the world. For us and our successors, that experience is beyond reach.

3 TIMES HAVE CHANGED:

Twentieth-Century Conservation

Populations of many native game animals in Texas plunged to all-time lows in the first two decades of the present century before law enforcement effectively curtailed indiscriminate hunting. The long uphill struggle for a number of species involved the active cooperation of wildlife biologists and landowners, both of whom made strenuous efforts to stabilize populations and provide a breeding nucleus for recovery.

Federal laws also helped. International treaties regulating hunting and trade, specifically the Migratory Bird Treaty Act of 1916, gave national officials powers to set the framework for conserving waterfowl, cranes, shorebirds, doves, and other species migrating between Canada and the United States. The treaty's regulations dealt a severe blow to market hunting. It prohibited live decoys and baits, limited the types of weapons used for hunting, and established closed seasons.

Perhaps the most important support for state conservation, and certainly the most constructive in its intent, was the Pittman-Robertson Act of 1937, which established a program of federal aid by apportioning funds to state wildlife agencies from taxes levied on sporting arms and ammunition. So-called P-R funds went toward research into the life histories, habitat needs, and capture and transplant of important game animals, including pronghorn antelope and wild turkey in Texas. Both species have recovered sufficiently during the past half-century to once again afford recreation for hunters.

Of equal or greater importance for conservation efforts are the changing attitudes toward wild animals, even toward traditional pests like the alligator and red wolf. A century ago Texans shot those creatures on sight, in part because they were believed to prey on livestock and in part because they had no place in a settled and civilized society. Today, as most Texans live and work far removed from the land, the sight of wild animals stirs excitement and perhaps rekindles a nostalgic bond with primitive feelings and impulses. Charlie, an older alligator and tourist attraction at the Aransas National Wildlife Refuge, is a case in point. On a more practical level, however, conservation of the alligator reestablished a market for its meat and hide. The preservation of the red wolf is a more difficult case to justify, both on biological and cultural grounds. Like its cousin the coyote, the wolf has received short shrift, but its doglike characteristics have won over increasing numbers of people, while others support its preservation because it is now so rare.

BACK FROM THE BRINK: *The Pronghorn and the Turkey*

Both the pronghorn antelope and the wild turkey experienced species-threatening population losses over the last century. Fortunately, such losses were recognized in time to implement efforts to conserve both animals. Those efforts included new management techniques addressing the needs of each species and helped pull the pronghorn and the wild turkey from the brink of extinction.

> Give me a home where the buffalo roam
> and the deer and the antelope play

We are all familiar with the lyrics from "Home on the Range," and chances are that the above lines were just now read with a hint of the melody among the words. The song gives a glimpse of the open range – a bucolic scene in which herds of animals graze peacefully under a cloudless blue sky. But have we ever stopped to think about the actual landscape that inspired those words?

In the early 1840s, William Bollaert, a British geographer traveling

Pronghorn Antelope

through Texas, remarked that the "graceful" antelope frequented the open, wide, and unobstructed plains and prairies where the "powerful" bison also ranged. The number of pronghorn was said to be comparable to that of the buffalo, which meant that tens of millions of the animals must have grazed on the western plains. The deer in "Home on the Range" are most likely mule deer, which ranged in west Texas from the High Plains through the Trans-Pecos. As the song suggests, mule deer and antelope sometimes foraged together.

Unique to North America and a native mammal of Texas, the pronghorn antelope (*Antilocapra americana*) is the only surviving genus and species of the family Antilocapridae, which evolved in North America 15 million years ago. Thirteen additional members of the ruminant family existed during the Pliocene and Pleistocene but died out, leaving only the pronghorn to carry on. Although it shares the antelope name with other species in Africa and Asia, most experts do not believe that it is directly related to those creatures and restrict the family to North America's grasslands.

The pronghorn is named for its black forked horns. The male's horns reach beyond the tips of the ears; the female's are shorter and seldom pronged. The overall tan color is shaded from a light tan on the legs to a dark cinnamon along the back and neck. Highly visible patches of white mark the animal's sides, and two white bands extend across the throat. Its long white rump hairs are rooted in a sheath of muscle tissue, which allows an animal to flare the hairs when it senses danger. That signal serves as a warning to other antelopes, who can see it even from several miles away.

The cloven-hoofed pronghorn is the fleetest of North American mammals, capable of reaching a top speed of 45 miles an hour. Its swiftness, combined with exceptional farsighted vision, provides the antelope with its primary means of defense against predators such as wolves and cougars. In addition, the protrusion of its large eyes gives the pronghorn a broad field of vision.

In the 1800s, the pronghorn antelope numbered perhaps 35 million or more in the United States and reportedly existed in large numbers throughout the western portions of Texas, especially on the extensive grasslands of the high and rolling plains as far east as the blackland prairie (beyond present-day Waco), and south into the Rio Grande Plain.

Travelers and plainsmen admired the pronghorn's grace and agility and eagerly hunted it as a game animal. Pronghorns have the habit of investigating objects, including wagons and people, that seem out of place in their open and relatively flat environment. That streak of curiosity cost the animals dearly. Partially concealed hunters had only to wave a bright cloth at distant herds to lure a few creatures into range. Settlement, ranching, fencing, and a growing demand for meat, combined with improved firearms and sport hunting, reduced pronghorn numbers to an all-time low by the mid-twenties, and the pronghorn seemed on the verge of extinction. Intensive efforts by state biologists and local ranchers were required to save the few remaining fragmented herds. At that time about 2,400 animals lived in small bands in forty West Texas counties, and about 700 others survived west of the Pecos River. Texas held about 10 percent of North America's pronghorns, whose numbers had dropped to about 27,000.

Excessive hunting was the principal cause of the mammal's decline, but other factors contributed to a collapse in numbers. Natural hazards, including predation by golden eagles on fawns, blizzards, drought, and even hailstorms, took their tolls. The demand for wheat, cotton, and small grains brought about the conversion of many thousands of acres of optimum pronghorn habitat into farmland, and ranchers strung fences across much of the remaining rangeland in the Trans-Pecos, used primarily for sheep. Pronghorns will seldom jump over obstacles higher than three feet, so sheep-proof fences also confined antelope and disrupted their seasonal movements and their need to forage widely. Pronghorns are much more dependent upon forbs (such as paper daisies and goldeneye) than are sheep; therefore, in heavily stocked areas where sheep had eliminated those plants, the antelope, unable to feed beyond the fences, often starved. Drought exacerbated that form of distress, causing animals to subsist on browse and die of malnutrition and blackbush poisoning.

Between 1939 and 1944, under the provisions of the P-R program, state biologists supervised the capture and transport of 1,386 pronghorn antelope from areas in the Trans-Pecos for release in 34 counties throughout west Texas as part of a restocking program. The transplanted animals have formed the nucleus for rebuilding the pronghorn population. By 1944, numbers in Texas totaled about 9,000 antelope. Restoration in the Trans-Pecos region enabled Texans to hunt the antelope legally in the fall of 1944—the first time in more than forty years—during which 297 antelope were killed in a closely monitored hunt. The pronghorn antelope thus became the first game mammal in Texas to have its populations artificially restocked, managed, and harvested on a sustained basis. About 6,000 animals have been stocked by state authorities since 1938, and some have been shipped to Arizona in exchange for desert bighorns. Pronghorn numbers peaked in 1961 at 12,000 animals before a drought took a severe toll.

The rehabilitation of the pronghorn in Texas is an excellent example of how management for an endangered game animal can be used not only to stabilize a population but also to increase its numbers so that hunting once again becomes possible. Research concerning the life history, behavior, range use, and proper harvest of the pronghorn antelope has been a crucial element in developing successful wild herd management techniques. The pronghorn has increased nationwide by more than 3,000 percent in the past sixty years; today it numbers in excess of one million animals, of which about 25,000 roam ranges in Texas.

Benjamin Franklin was dismayed when the Continental Congress of 1782 voted to put the image of a bald eagle on the Great Seal of the United States. The eagle, he fumed in a letter to his daughter, was lazy, dishonest, and a "rank coward." And what did Franklin favor as an alternative? The wild turkey, of course, that bird unique to the New World, whose meat had provided sustenance to the Pilgrims and the pioneers who succeeded them. Though Franklin acknowledged that the turkey was perhaps a little "vain and silly," it was at least a bird of distinction and thus was a more fitting symbol for the new republic. Despite losing out to the eagle, the turkey has retained its popularity as the largest and most colorful of our upland game birds. And in Texas, its numbers are once again booming.

Although we associate the domestic turkey with awkwardness and clumsiness, its wild counterpart is surprisingly fast and agile in dodging through the woody growth of its preferred habitat. The iridescent metallic tones of green, bronze, and blue lend the wild turkey dramatic color and account for its name *Meleagris gallopavo*, meaning a peacocklike fowl. The beautiful color and texture of its feathers contrast sharply with the bird's naked head, neck, and fleshy wattles. Endemic to North America, the turkey impressed early European explorers with its large size (up to four feet in length), weight (15 pounds or more), and wingspan (in excess of five feet). Indians hunted the wild turkey in the East but never domesticated it, as the Aztecs did in Old Mexico, where the Spanish first discovered it. Cortés described it and carried specimens back to Spain; ironically, when English colonists later sailed to North America, they brought a domesticated version of the New World turkey with them.

The impact of European civilization on the North American landscape was swift in coming. While clearing the path for a New World society, settlers inflicted severe losses upon native wildlife, including the wild turkey. The clearing of forest cover, combined with vastly increased hunting and trapping pressures, completely eliminated the wild turkey in many eastern states. Aboriginal range included all or portions of 39 states, but today in 19 of them (including Ohio, Indiana, and much of New England), the turkey no longer survives in the wild.

Three varieties of the wild turkey once roamed throughout Texas. Merriam's wild turkey (*Meleagris gallopavo merriami*) inhabited the highlands of west Texas, particularly the Guadalupe Mountains. The

Wild Turkey

eastern wild turkey (*Meleagris gallopavo silvestris*) had the run of oak and pine woodlands east of about longitude 97 degrees west, from Gulf lowlands to Missouri and east to Maine. The Rio Grande turkey (*Meleagris gallopavo intermedia*), the largest and most abundant of the three subspecies, ranged over much of the remainder of Texas westward to near the Pecos River and northward into Oklahoma's Panhandle.

Together, the three varieties of wild turkey numbered into the millions, some say 7 million to 10 million; but with the advent of nineteenth-century settlement, populations rapidly declined. Settlers shot them for food, cleared the woodlands for crops and livestock, and freed their hogs in the remaining forests, where they competed with the turkey for food and rooted out its nests. By 1928, decades of overhunting, deforestation, and intensive grazing by domestic livestock, combined with predation, floods, and drought, had brought the turkey's population to less than 100,000. The eastern race had fared the worst since its woodland habitat had undergone the most change. Experts believe that the eastern wild bloodstock was extirpated by the mid-forties.

Although the first step in protecting the wild turkey was taken more than a century ago, it was only in the twenties that state funds for game wardens made it possible to significantly cut into poaching. With illegal hunting under control, state authorities turned their attention to the restoration of the turkey to areas from which it had been extirpated. The process of trapping and relocating turkeys began early in the twenties in Sutton and Kerr counties and gained momentum as federal funds became available in the late thirties and forties. In the forties, state game officials began to compile records detailing the original numbers and areas of relocation. Between 1938 and 1961, a total of 8,629 turkeys were relocated within the state; in 1942, the peak year, 1,005 Rio Grande turkeys were transplanted to 36 Texas counties.

Transplants have had variable success. The release of the Rio Grande race of wild turkey into eastern counties tested the ability of the western dryland birds to adapt to the humid, forested habitat of east Texas. Most birds failed to adjust. In the early sixties, authorities imported turkeys from Florida in hope that they would be better suited to southeast Texas. Although they proved more successful than the Rio Grande turkey, their reproduction rates were still too low. A wildlife swap in 1978 finally got the eastern bird on the road to recovery. Texas pheasants were sent to Louisiana in exchange for some of the latter's turkeys, close cousins to those of east Texas, and they appear to be thriving along with others from Mississippi and Oklahoma. The first Louisiana turkeys released in Texas were banded, tagged, and fitted with lightweight radio transmitters so that game managers and researchers could track their locations, movements, reproduction, and mortality. Other studies, involving birds from other states, have explored habitat preferences and responses to various management practices.

The research makes clear that the successful restoration of wild turkeys, especially sensitive eastern birds, requires the improvement of native habitat, not just transplanting them from one region to another. Experts suggest that birds do best in habitat similar to that where they originated. Ideally, release points should be in the center of a sizable area (at least 8,300 hectares) of good range, with grassy openings, herbaceous vegetation (encouraged by prescribed burning and forest thinning), and, optimally, food plots planted with grains. Deferring grazing or rotating livestock promotes growth of natural foods. Bottomland provides important winter territory where turkeys can fatten up for the breeding season on acorns and other high-energy foods. Releasing birds well ahead of the spring nesting period increases the probability of success by giving individuals time to investigate and adjust to new habitat opportunities and to the activities of other birds in the release areas. Although experts have developed those management policies, the key to success obviously lies with the cooperation of private landowners.

The path to turkey recovery has been well and truly laid in Texas, even for the hard-pressed eastern race in the pine and hardwood zone. The Texas chapter of the National Wild Turkey Federation has helped keep the forces of extinction at bay while transplant programs, from South Carolina in 1987, for example, have enabled populations to be restocked. Increasing numbers of ranchers and landowners are interested in maintaining the wild turkey on their property and are prepared to consult biologists about optimizing conditions for the king of game birds. Jim Dickson and Charles Allen have noted (in *Texas Parks and Wildlife* magazine, March 1989) that there are about 1,500 wild turkeys in east Texas and millions of acres of good habitat awaiting more of them. Ben Franklin could take some

American Alligator

solace in knowing that two million to three million of his courageous turkeys still roam the nation and that the gobbler is doing well in an ancestral stronghold – Texas.

FROM PEST TO RESOURCE: *The American Alligator*

Crocodilians have been living on Earth for approximately 200 million years. The alligator belongs to one of eight families of living crocodilians (order *Crocodilia*), which are widely distributed from tropical Southeast Asia and North Australia to India, throughout much of South and Central Africa, and north along the River Nile to the shores of the Mediterranean Sea (where the Nile crocodile is now extremely rare). New World crocodilians inhabit moist lowlands from southern Brazil to Central America and occur in many islands of the Caribbean. The American alligator (*Alligator mississippiensis*) is the northernmost species, ranging from coastal North Carolina south through Florida across to central Texas and up the Mississippi watershed as far as southern Arkansas and southeast Oklahoma.

Despite the enticements of roadside zoos advertising "thousand-year-old gators," alligators generally grow senile, lose their teeth, and die before they reach the half-century mark. Although sometimes confused with the American crocodile, whose U.S. range is confined to extreme southern Florida, the alligator is distinguished by a broad rounded snout; the crocodile's is narrow and sharply tapered. Weighing up to 450 kilograms, alligators are also heavier than American crocodiles and much darker, often nearly black, in contrast to the crocodile's light-gray or olive-green color. The alligator's massive teeth are used only for capturing prey and not for chewing it; its powerful digestive juices perform the task of breaking down food. Alligator diets generally include turtles, fish, snakes, birds, and aquatic or riparian mammals such as nutria and raccoons. The size of the alligator, ranging from three to twelve feet or more in length, largely determines what size prey it will attack.

In Texas, the American alligator once ranged as far north as the Red River, west to near Dallas, southwest to San Antonio, and into the South Texas Plain; precisely where is uncertain and debated. Within that area, the alligator preferred brackish coastal marshes, rivers, and freshwater swamps and marshes, as well as natural and artificial lakes and ponds in east and south Texas. The loss of those wetlands contributed to the alligator's earlier decline.

Throughout the southeastern United States, millions of square miles of marshes have been drained, primarily for agricultural production, destroying prime alligator habitat. Even where wetlands remain, fluctuating water levels caused by dikes, dams, and diversion channels interfere with alligator reproduction. Dams also act as barriers to alligator dispersal and decrease the quality of habitat downstream. In addition, the post–World War II boom in outdoor recreation opened up marshes to airboats and all-terrain vehicles, which further disturbed alligators, giving hunters greater access to them. An area of prime coastal mainland in southeast Texas and Louisiana decreased by 20 percent in the period from 1952 to 1974. Such disturbances and losses have forced the alligator into marginal and less secure habitats.

The spread of alligators into marginal and unfamiliar places sometimes brings them face to face with humans, especially in suburban areas near coastal marshes. Florida residents have formed a "gator watch" to remove troublesome individuals. Although alligators have attacked people in a few instances (one mauled a swimmer in Cypress Lake, near Orange, Texas, in August 1985) they usually avoid humans. The reptile has also run into conflict with some ranchers and farmers who blame it for livestock losses and damage to the banks of canals and stock ponds.

Overhunting of the American alligator was primarily responsible for its decline. People had no qualms about shooting such a menacing-looking creature, and gator-killing was a genial sport frequently practiced along the Mississippi River, where passengers on paddle steamers relieved boredom by blasting away at reptiles sunning themselves. Early settlers hunted the alligator for its meat and hide, which they worked into leather, and also killed it out of fear or because of reported predation on livestock. By 1870, alligator leather was highly fashionable, and hunters killed them by the thousands. Numbers dwindled, and by the mid-sixties the combination of relentless overhunting and habitat loss had brought the American alligator close to extinction.

Accordingly, in 1967, the alligator was included in the list of species endangered throughout their range. In 1969, Texas closed its hunting season on alligators, and the federal government prohibited the interstate shipment of gator skins. Conservation practices in the United States have enabled the reptile to make a stunning comeback. By the mid-seventies, numbers had increased to 738,000 nationally and by 1981 to more than one million in ten states. Most of them were in Florida and Louisiana. Since then, the population has grown rapidly; by 1986, an estimated quarter of a million alligators inhabited the wetlands of Texas.

The J. D. Murphree Wildlife Management Area in Jefferson County, Texas, offers an example of optimum alligator habitat. It consists of 11.4 square miles of brackish and freshwater marsh and includes leveed areas in which salinity and water level are controlled to maintain a wetland suitable for waterfowl and the alligator. Nesting and reproduction proceed relatively undisturbed in the marshes, and protection from hunters and recreationists has resulted in a steadily increasing population.

In 1981, the dramatic upturn in numbers led the Texas Parks and Wildlife Department to request that the U.S. Fish and Wildlife Service reclassify the status of the American alligator in the state. At that time, approximately 90,000 alligators inhabited Jefferson, Chambers, and Orange counties, and state biologists were arguing for a selective harvest to head off potential problems of a population explosion (under the existing regulations, Parks and Wildlife personnel had authority to capture or kill only individual nuisance alligators). The situation was getting especially serious in Port Arthur, where state biologists had removed well over a hundred of the creatures from within the city limits. Residents complained of finding gators beneath their houses or in swimming pools and back yards. One nine-foot gator was taken from the parking lot of a fast-food restaurant in downtown Port Arthur; it had apparently wandered along a drainage ditch before emerging near the city center.

Efforts to change the status of the American alligator succeeded. In October 1983, the classifications "threatened" in coastal areas and "endangered" in other parts of Texas became uniformly listed as "threatened due to similarity of appearance"—the least restrictive category under the Endangered Species Act. The new listing guaranteed that strict federal rules would continue to regulate commerce in Texas alligator products (since they cannot be distinguished from those originating in other states where the alligator is still threatened or endangered) but gave Texas authority to manage and protect alligators within its own borders.

The new classification made it possible for the Parks and Wildlife Department to begin a regulated harvest (already permitted in Louisiana). The next year, 437 Texas gators were bagged, then 747 in 1985, and 1,644 in 1988—the largest, from Eagle Lake, measured 13 feet 5 inches. Hunters can use a hook and line, harpoon, or handheld snare but cannot shoot the reptiles except to finish off snagged individuals. If population trends continue, and hunting remains well regulated, the American alligator will be acknowledged as both a valuable economic resource and as a respected resident of Texas wetlands.

GENETIC SWAMPING: *The End of the Red Wolf*

The wolf has long been a favorite in stories of folklore and adventure, a savage character menacing man and beast. Fantastic tales about wolves chasing down people and seizing defenseless animals reflect the prejudices of past and present generations and create inherited myths that we may pass off as facts. Wolf legends exemplify the human belief in nature as "red in tooth and claw."

Within that fabric of myth and superstition lies the tale of the red wolf, *Canis rufus*. The lone wolf of legend is actually a social creature that hunts, feeds, and travels in a pack. Red wolves usually mate for life, denning in heavy cover or, in the case of its final stronghold on the Gulf Coast prairie, in low, sandy mounds and raising litters of three to six pups. Its name is misleading; its fur color may appear cinnamon, gray, yellow, or tawny with gray and black. Its muzzle is often light in color, and a tan spot over each eye accentuates its slanted-eye appearance.

Early observations of the red wolf described it as a long-legged, rangy animal, and it is the long and slender legs that enable it to cross large stretches of territory. A second characteristic of the red wolf is the large size of its ears in relation to its skull. Larger and more robust than the coyote, for whom it is often mistaken, but smaller than the gray wolf, an adult male red wolf weighs between 49 and 80 pounds (22 to 36 kilograms).

Much to the detriment of conservation efforts, little is known about the life history of *Canis rufus*, though it was first described by the explorer William Bartram in 1791. Biologists believe that there were at one time three different subspecies in the southeast United States. The wolves ranged in pairs and close family units throughout the forests and coastal prairies from the Atlantic coast to central Texas and as far north as Virginia, central Missouri, and southern Illinois. By 1920, the red wolf had vanished from most areas east of the Mississippi River and from most of central and northeast Texas, central Oklahoma, and southeastern Kansas. In 1940, records reveal small numbers of the only extant subspecies, *C. r. gregoryi*, surviving

Red Wolf

in the Big Thicket and coastal areas of Texas and Louisiana, along with a few individuals scattered across southwest Oklahoma, southern Arkansas, southern Mississippi, and sections of extreme western Alabama.

During the next three decades, its range continued to shrink. By the late seventies, the wolf was restricted in Texas to Jefferson and Orange counties south of Interstate Highway 10 and to Cameron and

Calcasieu parishes in Louisiana. Today, biologists consider the red wolf to be extirpated from the wild, though the presence of hybrids produced by the mating of red wolves with coyotes makes absolute determination of its status difficult. Certainly no viable wild population of true red wolves exists, and attention is now focused on maintaining and increasing what people believe are genetically pure stocks in captivity.

The decline of the red wolf began, not surprisingly, with the growth and expansion of human populations in the southeastern U.S. The wolf, like many other animals, suffered from the clearing of land for crops and timber. One habitat requirement for the red wolf appears to be good vegetation cover, especially along waterways. Areas with dense woody plants provide secure resting and denning sites. The bayous and overgrown thickets along coastal lowlands were the last places the wolf survived in southeast Texas and southwest Louisiana, probably because they were unpromising for human settlement. The wolf likewise encountered difficulties in the damp, mosquito-ridden lowlands, mostly in the form of parasite infestations. Heartworm (*Dirofilaria immitis*) was an especially serious problem; in a 1972 study, the U.S. Fish and Wildlife Service found the parasite in all 27 wolves it examined. Other common parasites include hookworms and tapeworms. Heavy infestations further weaken the wolf's ability to deal with stress; research indicates that most of the pups die of hookworm before they reach six months of age.

Predator control programs have also been a major cause of mortality. Human dislike of the red wolf led to the establishment of the bounty system. Widespread shooting by farmers and ranchers, the construction of wolf-proof fences, and the use of steel traps and poison baits cut into numbers substantially. Until President Nixon's executive order banning Compound 1080 in February 1972, farmers and ranchers frequently used the deadly poison to kill coyotes and wolves. (The ban was lifted in 1982 in response to complaints of unreasonable livestock losses, and the use of single-dose baits of Compound 1080 in toxic collars attached to goats and sheep is now permitted.) Unlike its larger cousin, the gray wolf, however, *Canis rufus* has never been regarded as a serious threat to livestock. It will take untended calves and sometimes pigs, poultry, and goats, but generally the red wolf shies away from man and his activities, subsisting instead on smaller animals and on plant foods.

Hybridization may have sealed the red wolf's fate. As numbers decreased, the coyote, who is able to live almost anywhere and eat almost anything, began to move into the western edges of the red wolf's range. The two species mated readily, leading to a steadily increasing and finally irreversible dilution of red wolf genes. Hybridization reportedly began on the Edwards Plateau in the early 1900s, and by the forties coyote-wolf crosses had appeared in several localities in east Texas. Thirty years later, hybrids occurred throughout the Pineywoods region, and relatively pure red wolves remained only on the lowlands of the upper Gulf Coast.

After the initial taxonomic confusion caused by the interbreeding of wolves with coyotes and even feral dogs, canid specialists established a list of five characteristics that distinguish hybrids from true red wolves. Specifically, hybrids have (1) smaller legs and feet, (2) shorter ears, (3) a less massive muzzle, (4) a smaller overall size, and (5) a coyotelike threat posture, which includes an arched back and tucked tail. Based on those criteria, a March 1980 report by the U.S. Fish and Wildlife Service judged that fewer than 50 pure red wolves existed in the wild.

On March 11, 1967, the red wolf was listed as a federally protected endangered species, and a recovery program was drawn up. With the 1973 Endangered Species Act, the red wolf began to receive priority treatment. U.S. Fish and Wildlife Service personnel began capturing the canids in Texas and Louisiana during the late seventies to bolster genetic diversity for captive breeding. Although some questioned the wisdom of further depleting the already dwindling wild population, biologists concluded that the wolf's extinction in the wild appeared inevitable and that the removal of the remaining animals provided the only practical solution for preserving the species. Efforts to capture wolves ended in September 1980, when biologists determined that too few, if any, wolves were left to justify their continued search. By that time, some 400 canids had been trapped, but of those, only 40 were judged to be pure red wolves.

The 40 pure wild-caught red wolves eventually came under the care of Dale Pedersen, owner of United Farms, a mink breeding facility in Graham, Washington. His change of fortune is not as strange as it may sound. In addition to his interest in endangered wildlife, Pedersen had acquired a good deal of expertise in captive breeding while operating his mink business. The Point Defiance Zoo in Tacoma,

Washington, had originally begun a captive breeding program in 1973; its distance from the wolf's home also isolated the animals from heartworm and other parasites endemic to the coastal areas of Texas and Louisiana. The Point Defiance Zoo later engaged Pedersen to assist in its efforts to save the embattled canid.

In the end, only 14 of the captured wolves who produced young turned out to be pure red wolves, and with those 14 as founding parents, Pedersen set to work. With such a limited stock, it was vital that the wolves be bred so as to ensure that eventually each captive-born wolf would carry the genes of all 14 original wild wolves. Although Pedersen himself disliked what he called the Orwellian aspects of the obsession with genes and purity, in the wolf's case it was essential for the survival of a strong and healthy population. By August 1986, the captive breeding program had produced 80 pure red wolves, most born at Pedersen's facilities and others in affiliated breeding projects.

In the meantime, the feasibility of releasing captive-bred red wolves in the wild came under scrutiny. The initial success of a one-year experiment in 1978 that released a pair of wolves on Bull Island, South Carolina, encouraged those hoping for the wolf's reestablishment. But subsequent efforts to locate other suitable areas for reintroduction proved frustrating. Public opposition arose from fears about the menacing wolf. Farmers and ranchers were concerned about livestock, and hunters argued that the wolf would deplete deer and turkeys. Such concerns might be more appropriate for the timber wolf, but for the small and shy red wolf they are misplaced. Apart from those obstacles, however, there remained the problem of finding a site large enough to ensure the wolf's survival away from human pressures and also free of coyotes and enticements to interbreed.

After several false starts, the U.S. Fish and Wildlife Service announced in 1986 that it had selected the Alligator River National Wildlife Refuge on the North Carolina coast for a new reintroduction effort. The inhabitants of Dare County, where the refuge is located, live mostly off fishing, not livestock, and so did not oppose the wolf's presence to the degree other communities had. In addition, the county's woody swamps and marshes are already home to bears, bobcats, and alligators, so the equally wily human residents were not alarmed at the thought of a few more critters. "As long as I can dog-hunt," said one man in response to the government's proposal, "I don't care if they turn a rhinoceros loose." Though not everyone was as blasé, the service was able to negotiate to allow residents to shoot wolves off the refuge if they threatened human safety and property, although killing is normally prohibited under the Endangered Species Act.

In November 1986, the first four pairs of wolves arrived in the refuge, where they lived in large pens for ten months to acclimatize to their new home. Refuge personnel fed them small animals native to the area, hoping the wolves would develop a taste for local prey. In September 1987, biologists released them away from disturbances. The occasion marked the first time in North American history that a species considered extinct in the wild had returned to it with human help. By December, two of the wolves, both females, had died, one apparently from an infection and one from wounds perhaps received in a fight with another wolf. Biologists and refuge staff remained optimistic, nevertheless, as the public responded to the wolves' presence with interest and enthusiasm, even when one roamed into the outskirts of a nearby town before its capture by refuge workers. The six surviving wolves appear to have adapted well to the refuge, feeding on small deer, raccoons, and other mammals. There are plans to add additional wolves to the area. The Fish and Wildlife Service is also planning to release, temporarily, captive-bred wolves on Bull Island again, let them breed, then capture the wild-born offspring for transfer to permanent reintroduction areas.

New release prospects have raised hopes that the red wolf will not be relegated to merely a zoo curiosity. On the other hand, if the program fails, the wolf may be in deeper trouble, since additional funding for reintroduction will be hard to come by. Acknowledging that release may not succeed, the American Association of Zoological Parks and Aquariums agreed in 1984 to develop a species survival plan for the wolf. The plan will coordinate the management of all captive populations at participating institutions in an effort to maintain as large a gene pool as possible. The Texas Zoo in Victoria, which specializes in animals and birds native to the state, is one of the zoos in the plan. The zoo's resident female wolf has bred successfully in the past. She and her new mate, assigned to the zoo by the Fish and Wildlife Service in 1985, have yet to breed, but zoo personnel remain hopeful. In the meantime, the pair offers a rare view of a species that had nearly vanished from our midst.

Although captive breeding is salutory in that it preserves the red wolf from complete extinction, a future behind fences is surely a bleak one. Reintroduction is our and the wolf's best hope, but even if it succeeds, *Canis rufus* will never roam wild and free as it once did. The wolves introduced in the Alligator River Refuge carry high-technology collars fitted with radio transmitters capable of being pinpointed by airplane. Also on the collars are two tranquilizing darts to be injected into the animal's neck on radio command from overflying aircraft if he or she wanders off the refuge. Although those measures are not meant to be permanent, they illustrate well the state of the art in contemporary wildlife management and remind us that even in our conservation successes there is much we have lost.

4 THE JURY IS STILL OUT

The mountain sheep (bighorn), black bear, and Attwater's greater prairie chicken represent animals that were once plentiful within the boundaries of Texas. They exist in greatly reduced populations because of two principal factors: human predation and habitat loss. State and federal authorities have cooperated in research into mountain sheep and the prairie chicken, but numbers of each species remain low, as do those of the black bear. Some experts seriously doubt whether any of them will ever significantly increase in the future.

The whooping crane and Eskimo curlew are migratory birds. The former winters on the Texas coast, and the latter pauses there for a few days or weeks in spring. Federal laws have protected the birds for seventy years, and they are listed as endangered species. The crane and curlew exemplify two ends of the spectrum of conservation. The whooping crane symbolizes America's commitment to endangered wildlife. This rare, tall, splendid-looking waterbird has responded well to efforts aimed at protecting and managing its relict population. From widespread media coverage, the public knows a great deal about the whooper's movements, numbers, and life history.

At the other end of the spectrum, almost nothing is publicized about the smaller, drab shorebird, the Eskimo curlew, which may just be hanging onto existence by nesting in the Canadian Arctic. Texas birders occasionally report one or two curlews when the sleek, fleet migrant makes landfall on Galveston Island in April or May on a long journey from wintering grounds on the shortgrass prairies of southern South America. Unlike similar shorebirds subjected to unregulated hunting toward the close of the nineteenth century, the Eskimo curlew has not responded to protection. The highly edible and gregarious birds fell before the guns of market men and sport hunters who fired into dense flocks as they spun their way north across the plains into Canada. Again, it is too soon to close the book on the Eskimo curlew as we have on the ivory-billed woodpecker. It is also too soon to congratulate ourselves for ensuring that the whooping crane will survive into the twenty-first century. The curlew is not extinct; the whooping crane's survival is not assured. In that sense, the jury has yet to reach a verdict as to whether those animals, plus others such as the bighorn sheep and prairie chicken, will survive.

The Mountain Sheep in the Trans-Pecos

A recent issue of *Texas Parks and Wildlife* magazine characterized the mountain sheep, or desert bighorn (*Ovis canadensis*), program as wavering between "modest optimism and despair." Optimism stems from enthusiastic attempts over the last twenty years to restore the mountain sheep to upland terrain in the Trans-Pecos. There is despair too, because after limited success in propagation with animals imported from Arizona, Mexico, Utah, and Nevada, bighorn numbers have once again faltered in response to disease, predation, and nutritional stress. Biologists have repeatedly hoped for the species' recovery, but until recently, losses of the introduced animals have jeopardized intensive (and expensive) efforts to reinstate the bighorn to Texas. The losses are particularly frustrating in light of the success of the bighorn's North African relative, the aoudad, or Barbary sheep (*Ammotragus lervia*), which was released in 1957 into Palo Duro Canyon, where it became so well established that state authorities allowed a controlled hunt to begin six years later.

The mountain sheep is a large, dark brown ungulate with a white rump patch. Males weigh up to 340 pounds (154 kilograms) and sport heavy, curled, tapering horns. The noble-looking animal encountered difficulties more than a century ago. Railroad construction

Bighorn Sheep

gangs built the Texas and Pacific line between El Paso and the east at about the same time miners after silver ore deposits moved into the bighorn's stronghold, the Beach, Baylor, and Diablo mountains in far west Texas. Both railroad gangs and miners hunted deer, antelope, and bighorn sheep.

Burch Carson from Van Horn in Culberson County, who conducted a 1940 state survey on the bighorn, addressed the story of overhunting. He discovered that the Hazel Mine, north of Van Horn, which operated from 1882 to 1896, played a significant role in the destruction of the magnificent, agile animal. Miners, more than 400 of them in peak years, used leisure time for hunting, and the bighorn became a favorite target. One old-timer told Carson that if the silver mine had not shut down, the bighorn "would have long since been extinct, like the passenger pigeon."

Human predation came from another direction as well. As railroad workers pushed into the Van Horn area in 1881, the new route attracted market hunters who, having whittled down bison in the Panhandle, turned their attention to mammals in the Trans-Pecos.

Refrigerated railcars carried deer, pronghorn, and bighorn sheep carcasses to urban markets.

The same combination of mining and railroads had identical results on bighorn populations in the Chisos, Glass, Chinati, and Vieja ranges. Additionally, introduction of sheep led to competition for forage and to the spread of domestic sheep diseases such as bluetongue among bighorn. Populations plummeted; by 1903, when the Legislature imposed restrictions on hunting bighorns, the wild mountain sheep had been nearly extirpated from the Big Bend area, according to Carson.

The spread of goat and sheep ranching and net wire fences in the Trans-Pecos continued to cause problems for remnant bighorns. In his 1940 study, Carson estimated that "there are not more than 150 bighorns in the three mountain ranges of the Beach, Diablo, and Baylor Mountains at the present time." As we have seen, the decline began sixty years earlier; predator control in the thirties provided some respite, but as domestic sheep filled the range, bighorns vanished. The last native mountain sheep were seen in the Sierra Diablo (where the Legislature established a 7,800-acre refuge in 1945) in 1960 when state personnel observed two ewes in Victoria Canyon.

Attempts to restore the bighorn have met with limited success. Initial efforts centered on conserving them in a 427-acre enclosure in the huge, 100,000-acre Black Gap Wildlife Management Area east of Big Bend National Park. Biologists staked out waterholes in Arizona's Kofa Game Range to trap bighorns, then transported them to Black Gap. Several transplants died from stress or injuries. Persistence and experience in handling sheep, however, paid off. By 1970, the Black Gap herd had risen to 68 head. In 1971, biologists set 20 sheep free; then disaster struck. Many of the remaining animals died from inadequate forage and disease (pneumonia and bluetongue), and the herd dropped quickly to ten adults and six lambs.

Cougars (mountain lions) also preyed on the Black Gap bighorns, killing 21 animals between 1975 and 1978, despite efforts to make the sheep enclosures predator-proof. So difficult had the situation become that the major thrust of the bighorn program was shifted from Black Gap to the Chilicote Ranch, in Presidio County, where a brood pasture was fenced in 1977. Some bighorns were also transported to the management area at Sierra Diablo. Releases in 1973 and

1979 from that facility led to the establishment of a free-ranging population, numbering presently as many as 100 head.

In 1986, approximately 100 bighorn sheep existed at four locations in Texas. Two years later the number had increased to about 275 at half a dozen sites. Disease and cougar predation have continued to plague the program, but with numbers on the upswing, biologists express guarded optimism. The recently founded Texas Bighorn Society is backing efforts at Sierra Diablo to develop brood stock imported from Nevada, Arizona, and Utah. Disease studies at the Glaze Veterinary Clinic in Kerrville have helped, and techniques for raising mountain sheep in captivity and releasing progeny into the wild have improved.

As of March 1987, the bighorn was not classified as threatened or endangered by state authorities, not because it is out of trouble but because captive and wild stock are subspecies imported from other states. The race *Ovis canadensis mexicana* no longer exists in Texas, and state wildlife experts do not consider it their obligation to list as endangered or threatened those artificially propagated populations that are not native to Texas. But regardless of legislative and taxonomic distinctions, it is good to think of mountain sheep once again roaming the uplands where they belong. If disease-related mortality in lambs can be dealt with adequately, then there is hope over the longer term. Currently, viruses originating from contact with domestic sheep suppress the immune systems of weaned lambs and cause many of them to die. In 1988, more than twenty lambs survived in the Sierra Diablo pens, a portent of improved survival. If efforts to increase disease-fighting antibodies succeed, then intensive management devoted to bighorns will have succeeded, and the species will achieve the status of a big-game mammal.

Attwater's Greater Prairie Chicken

Chicken cacciatore is tame fare compared with the tender prairie hen meat that Captain Flack, a famed hunter of marketable animals, recommended to merchant's wives in the 1850s. One of the species, Attwater's race of the greater prairie chicken (*Tympanuchus cupido attwateri*) is endemic to the midgrass coastal lowland, or what is left of it, ranging aboriginally from the northern edge of the Rio Grande Valley into western Louisiana.

Attwater's Greater Prairie Chicken

It is a brown, chickenlike bird, given as much to running as to flying, and is unobtrusive, except in spring when promiscuous males gather on open spaces, or booming grounds, to strut, posture, and fight over females in attendance. At dawn they send out deep booming noises from inflated air sacs on the sides of their necks and, in the excitement of their pre-mating ritual, become nearly oblivious to their surroundings.

Settlers capitalized on that trait and upon the bird's great abundance. They shot prairie chickens in large numbers, while settlement and land development whittled down prime habitat. The prairie chicken vanished from Louisiana around 1919; about a decade later, despite protection, fewer than 9,000 birds remained in Texas. Valgene Lehmann, who pioneered prairie chicken research in the thirties, argued that the dun-colored, grassland-bound species lacked the glamour of the wild turkey and received cursory attention. He suggested that unregulated hunting together with urban expansion (particularly in Harris County, an ancestral base) and ploughing for rice cultivation hit the species hard.

About 1,000 birds inhabited Colorado County in 1937, when 84,000 acres had already gone over to rice; since then another 40,000 acres of bluestem habitat have been lost, and only 300 or so birds remain. Today Colorado, Austin, and Refugio counties contain upwards of 75 percent of the state's population, numbering between 1,000 and 2,000 individuals, and most of the birds in Colorado County reside in Attwater's Prairie Chicken National Wildlife Refuge.

Management efforts began in the mid-sixties, and in 1967 the U.S. Fish and Wildlife Service listed the Attwater's race as endangered. Mr. and Mrs. J. M. Tatton donated 7,000 acres (2,833 hectares), upon which about twenty birds remain, to the Aransas National Wildlife Refuge, lending it the distinction of housing two of the nation's rarest birds: the whooping crane and Attwater's greater prairie chicken. The Prairie Chicken Refuge in Colorado County, near Eagle Lake, was purchased in the sixties and transferred to the U.S. Fish and Wildlife Service in 1972. It consists of 9,000 acres (3,240 hectares) of coastal prairie that is managed intensively to maximize its attractiveness for prairie chickens.

A 1983 federal recovery plan determined that "the outlook for the Attwater's greater prairie chicken is dim because of a continuing loss of habitat." Only one acre in seven of coastal prairie remains in Texas, although conditions are better in the three key counties where between one third and one quarter of aboriginal prairie acreage survives. But for the greater prairie chicken to maintain and increase its numbers, those areas require proper management to avoid excessive growth of unmodified prairie on the one hand and the loss of grass diversity through overgrazing and cultivation on the other. On the Attwater's Prairie Chicken Refuge, patches of grasses and forbs are maintained by autumn burning, moderate grazing, brush control, and mowing. Clumps of midgrass vegetation are best, consisting of little and big bluestem, tall dropseed, broomweed, Indiangrass, ragweed, and other forbs, with access to water and knolls or ridges nearby to help offset risks of flooding. Predation, especially from skunks, may severely inhibit population growth, so predator control is also a key to sound management.

At present, the deck seems stacked against the prairie chicken. Although there has been a significant increase from about 30 to 300 or so birds on refuge lands, biologists expect that the species will continue to dwindle and its range to shrink; it has already been extirpated from Galveston and Harris counties. Experts turned up fewer than 500 birds in March 1989, less than half the total for 1988 and a record low. Efforts for survival center on purchasing a second refuge in Goliad or Victoria counties and encouraging private landowners to conserve their birds and introduce grazing regimes that furnish good cover. Cattle and prairie chickens do mix, and even oil and gas extraction will not harm the species if care is taken to lessen human disturbance. The recovery team's goal of reducing the prairie chicken's listing to the "threatened" category by the year 2000, when it hopes the population will have reached 3,000, can only be met by stringent regard for habitat needs. That requires the active participation of private landowners on the coastal prairie. In the end, it will be the ranchers who decide the fate of this endangered subspecies.

The Whooping Crane

No other American animal exemplifies the public's commitment to endangered wildlife more than the whooping crane. It is one of the largest of the world's fifteen species of cranes, with black-tipped wings reaching out as far as a bald eagle's (7½ feet, or 2.4 meters). The loud bugling calls of this tall, graceful, and handsome crane once drifted across nesting marshes in the nation's interior. The whooping crane (*Grus americana*), one of two species in North America (the other is the much more populous, smaller, gray-brown sandhill crane), inhabited open, exposed wetlands in Illinois, northern Iowa, western Minnesota, and northeast North Dakota and ranged into Canada's prairie provinces, until human disturbance, marshland reclamation, and hunting drastically reduced its numbers. It last nested in the United States in 1889 and in Canada's aspen belt in Saskatchewan in 1922, when fewer than fifty birds remained. The breeding grounds of the remnant population that wintered on the Blackjack Peninsula, north of Rockport in Aransas County, Texas, remained unknown until 1954, when a pilot accidentally discovered them in the vast wilderness of the Sass River watershed in Canada's Wood Buffalo National Park, spanning the border of Alberta and the Northwest Territories. The birds migrate about 2,500 miles (3,800 kilometers) each way between Canada and Texas.

The whooping crane has existed for a million years and before the last Ice Age inhabited an area stretching from California to Georgia. In historic times, however, its range has been more restricted; some migrants wintered in Louisiana, Texas, and westward into coastal Mexico, while in the East, whoopers turned up regularly along the south Atlantic Seaboard. Reportedly never abundant in colonial America, as compared with its sandhill relative, the whooping crane's size, bearing, and color made it a prize. In Texas, a certain Captain Flack, a professional hunter, peddled deer, turkeys, and waterfowl in the 1850s. He recalled how hard the "big white cranes" were to stalk successfully, claiming that he had knocked down perhaps fifteen or so, in contrast to ten times that number of sandhill cranes, in many years of active hunting. Born hunter and naturalist Gideon Lincecum also remembered the bird's wariness. "Well, I didn't kill any, but speaking in bounds of reason, I think I came in two miles of it," he admitted ruefully after trying to bag one. Clearly there were bragging rights for securing a whooping crane in Texas.

Farmers with a keen eye for good soils had a more severe effect on cranes. As they siphoned away standing water from wetlands to reveal rich humus-laden clays, the crane's nesting habitat disappeared, and so did the birds.

What has followed has been a conservation odyssey—no other nongame bird species has received as much study, time, money, and

Whooping Crane

international cooperation, and today after fifty years the uphill battle to save wild whooping cranes continues. The story includes laws that prohibit hunting, establishment of refuges, captive rearing and breeding programs, and transplanting wild and captive-laid eggs under sandhill crane foster parents. Texas figures prominently in this conservation story.

When statistics began to be kept, the whooping crane population stood at a low ebb. In 1938, a year after the 55,000-acre (about 22,000 hectares) Aransas refuge was established, 18 whoopers wintered on the preserve, and 13 others formed a sedentary flock around White Lake, Louisiana. A decade later the situation had not improved. Although the number at Aransas had risen to 30 birds, a severe storm had decimated the Louisiana population, and in 1949 only one bird remained. Texas was left as the sole winter home for whooping cranes. The Aransas refuge offered security from November through about mid-April, when the birds migrated northward. After that time, refuge personnel could only wait and hope that numbers would be higher the next fall, when cranes, in pairs and small groups, spiraled down to the salt marshes. They looked for cinnamon-speckled young. The year 1949, in fact, proved a good one, as 30 adult-plumaged cranes brought in 4 young, but ten years would pass before there was an increase in those numbers.

Biologist Robert Porter Allen, working for the National Audubon Society with U.S. Fish and Wildlife Service cooperation, undertook crane research in Aransas in the late forties. Pennsylvania-born Allen deserves the title "Mr. Whooping Crane" for the painstaking way he pieced together the life history of the whooping crane. He set up a home in Austwell, near the refuge, in November 1946, and passed two winters observing cranes. He slogged across tide flats, poking into pools where birds fed, to determine where they lived and what they ate. He collected data about food habits, territory size and location, competition, and courtship and, through archival and museum research, reconstructed the bird's aboriginal range in North America.

Exasperated with watching his charges take wing, circle over the open wetlands and oak mottes on the Blackjack Peninsula, then head north in spring skies, Allen pushed north himself, traveling more than 20,000 miles in Canada searching for their nesting grounds. Although he was not the first to discover the remote breeding grounds, Allen was the first scientist to portage through the nearly impassable muskeg to survey whooper nest sites.

Robert P. Allen was a whooping crane zealot. The indomitable spirit of the big white bird possessed him as, with colleagues in Canada, he fought against the senseless shooting of cranes on migration. He also promoted efforts to pair up what few cranes there were in captivity. The famous pairing of Josephine, a Louisiana-caught female, with Crip, an adult male injured at Aransas, produced Rusty, the first captive-born chick. Sadly, raccoons probably snatched the chick within a day or so of hatching.

What has happened since Allen's pioneering research monograph was published in 1952? A little and a lot, depending on your perspective. Little has happened, in the sense that more than thirty years of crane research and management have failed to remove the bird from the endangered list. Despite all the expense, time, and effort, the fate of *Grus americana* remains uncertain.

On the other hand, a great deal has happened to offer encouragement. Ornithologists have broadened and deepened their knowledge of the bird's life history, most notably its reproduction and behavior. In 1967, after experiments to raise sandhill cranes in captivity, six whooper eggs were taken from nests in Canada's Wood Buffalo National Park and airlifted to a U.S. animal research center at Patuxent, near Laurel, Maryland. The objective was to raise whooping cranes in captivity and establish a flock whose progeny could be returned to the wild. The airlift was repeated in subsequent years after biologists confirmed that normally only one wild chick out of the clutch of two eggs survives. Subtracting an egg for artificial incubation did not depress the number of young arriving at Aransas; rather, young cranes in captivity could be a bonus saved from natural waste.

Difficulties related to nutrition, disease, and intraspecific competition hampered early breeding attempts when the fairly solitary birds found themselves housed together. But by 1970 the captive flock had risen to 22 birds; most were at Patuxent. In 1975, a Patuxent female crane laid the first eggs, and a year later some eggs from Patuxent were placed with others from Canada under wild sandhill cranes at a nesting area at Grays Lake, Idaho. Biologists have employed that technique, called cross fostering, to establish a second wild population, along the western fringe of the whooping crane's historic range. The greater sandhill crane belongs to the same genus (*Grus*) as the whooper and is the largest race of its species, not much smaller than its whooper cousin, although differing in vocalization and color. The sandhill foster parents accepted new clutches of eggs, raised the young whoopers as their own, and led them to winter quarters in New Mexico. In 1985, the Grays Lake flock numbered 34 whooping cranes. Unfortunately, no birds have paired off and raised young, and gradually the population dwindled to about half that number in 1988, when only 2 youngsters fledged from 12 transplanted eggs.

Work on whooping crane behavior has included detailed studies of banded individuals fitted with radio transmitters to follow their movements. Today, many wild cranes carry color bands so that human observers may tell them apart. By watching them at Aransas, for example, biologists have noted when and where newly formed pairs establish winter territories, how they defend them, and in later years how younger birds tend to return close to the areas they occupied in the company of their parents.

Ground and air coverage has enabled workers to follow the migratory pathways of radio-tagged birds. Trackers have found that migrating cranes cover varying distances each day, that individuals may occasionally fly at night, and, ominously, that power lines present hazards for the large, heavy avian. In recent years, several cranes in the Wood Buffalo–Aransas flock and in the Grays Lake flock have been killed or injured by flying into power lines and even fences.

Currently, most hunters are aware of the whooping crane's status and do not molest the birds. That is important, as single birds or pairs set down in stock ponds, even close to habitations, to rest and feed. So widespread is the concern about protecting them on migration that air traffic controllers at Dallas–Fort Worth International Airport once directed airplanes away from cranes that were passing close by.

The nation hopes that the whooping crane will not become a symbol of human folly, an example of a management plan *in extremis* that eventually failed. Numbers in the migratory wild population topped 136 in early 1989. We all hope that the crane—like another handsome white bird, the great egret, which rebounded amazingly after millinery interests ended their quest for its plumage—will stand for human success in the quest for a land ethic that allows all creatures to dwell in dignity.

The Eskimo Curlew

The tameness and sociability of the Eskimo curlew (*Numenius borealis*) may yet relegate this brown, curve-billed shorebird to the growing list of creatures that have become extinct this century.

Sometimes confused with the similar, larger whimbrel, the Eskimo curlew nested quite commonly but secretively on the open arctic tundra from the Mackenzie River region westward into Alaska and probably as far as the Bering Sea. Swift in flight, it wintered 10,000 miles to the south on the shortgrass prairies of interior South America, including the pampas of Argentina. In such remote, uninhabited breeding and wintering grounds, the bird never developed a fear of the human and, while migrating in large flocks through more-populated areas, was susceptible to close approach. Hunters blasted into compact masses of curlews, downing as many as thirty birds with one shot; excited sportsmen emptied wagons filled with carcasses to make room for more. From 1870 to 1890, the butchery reduced Eskimo curlew numbers so precipitously that by the early 1900s, ornithologists spoke of the bird as "practically extinct."

During late summer, adults and young headed east from breeding areas to staging points in Labrador, then they swung south and flew nonstop over the Atlantic Ocean to the Lesser Antilles and the coast of eastern South America, thence overland to southern grasslands. Fattened up for the long sea flight on crowberries, blueberries, and insects, the Eskimo curlew was eagerly awaited by fall hunters, who nicknamed it the doughbird. Southward-bound birds were so plump that when shot they sometimes burst open on impact with the ground. New England's wily coast and bay gunners destroyed entire flocks, especially after storms and hurricanes pushed tired migrants across shorelines.

The migration path in spring reportedly carried birds from the grasslands, over the Andes, and off the Pacific coast of South America to a landfall on the isthmus of Panama, then directly across the Gulf of Mexico to Louisiana and Texas. Upon arrival in April, the curlews ran the gauntlet of killing from the Gulf Coast through the western plains. A flock of "prairie pigeons" settling on open ground to forage for grasshopper egg pods, grubs, and worms could blanket 40 acres (16 hectares). Dense flocks of curlews reminded Audubon of passenger pigeon numbers; whether curlew or pigeon, such clouds of birds drew shotgun volleys as they took wing. That era of springtime gunning pushed the species to the brink of extinction.

One important question asks why the Eskimo curlew has not responded to protection, as did other shorebirds that suffered similar exploitation. Federal regulations for enforcing the 1916 Migratory

Eskimo Curlew

Bird Treaty Act banished market hunting and "game hogs," people who killed for the pleasure of tallying up large numbers. Such laws made it possible for migratory plovers, sandpipers, and godwits to build up numbers. Seventy years of continued protection have seen a steady if not spectacular growth among those bird populations, and none is listed currently as an endangered species. But the curlew still borders on extinction. There is no clear answer. Experts suggest that plowing up the tallgrass prairies, thereby reducing favorite food items such as grasshoppers, may be one factor. Others speculate that population numbers dropped below a critical level that made replacement impossible. Recent sightings, including a single bird on the Platte River in April 1987 and two birds on the Texas coast two weeks later, renewed hope for the Eskimo curlew's survival. In late May 1987, biologists of the Canadian Wildlife Service located a pair in the Canadian Artic, indicating that at least a small remnant of Eskimo curlews may be reproducing successfully. Why that population has not increased noticeably we do not know.

One place to look for the bird is Texas. The state is the major land terminus for the bird's lengthy overseas flight from winter quarters. Coastal marshlands provide food and rest for weary migrants, which continue northward over central Texas and the High Plains. Initially the Eskimo curlew was abundant on the coast in spring, but hunters had finished off those large flocks by 1900. Not a single sighting occurred from 1905 to 1945, when several observers identified two birds on Galveston Island, on April 29.

Between 1946 and 1968, another 9 sightings occurred, 6 of them from Galveston, 2 from Rockport, and 1 from the Aransas refuge, representing a total of 12 birds. May 7, 1981, is a memorable date for Eskimo curlew buffs. Two reputable ornithologists engaged in a bird census on Galveston Bay reported a flock of 23 Eskimo curlews. They observed the flock from 50 meters for less than a minute before the birds disappeared. The ornithologists suspected initially that the birds were whimbrels, but their smaller, ploverlike size, short decurved bill, and cinnamon-colored underwing linings visible in flight convinced the observers that they were seeing Eskimo curlews.

Reports, mostly unsubstantiated, of Eskimo curlews continue to come in from Texas. Galveston Island, close to the city of Galveston itself, remains the hot spot. It appears that the small "chittering curlew," as gunners called it, is tougher than people thought and is determinedly hanging on to existence. Whether there is sufficient protection from hunting in South America is hard to judge; because so few birds exist in so vast an area, they no doubt draw little attention to themselves. That may be the key to their durability.

5 New Concerns and Opportunities

Environmental legislation of the late sixties and the seventies, culminating with the 1973 Endangered Species Act, was a veritable civil rights manifesto for American wildlife. No longer did big game, exotic birds, or cute, humanlike mammals monopolize public attention and preservation efforts. The 1973 act ordered specific measures to be taken for protecting any plant or animal deemed to be threatened or endangered according to criteria laid down by the U.S. Fish and Wildlife Service.

The new law was the legislative manifesto for a new, broadened understanding of ecology, that is, the study of the vast network of interrelationships among living organisms and their environment. Within that network, even the smallest and most inconspicuous individuals ("non-resources," as David Ehrenfeld calls them) prove to have a role in the larger ecosystem. Likewise, animals traditionally judged to be harmful came to be appreciated for the part they played in nature. Indeed, nature itself was transformed in ecological thinking from an arena of tragedy and conflict where only the strongest (or luckiest) survive to a symphony of players, large and small, working in different ways to create a harmonious whole, a "comedy of survival," in the words of author Joseph Meeker.

Ecological research also explored why parts of the symphony appeared dangerously out of tune and showed that man's lauded virtuosity reverberated through the system in unexpected and often damaging ways. Direct harm from overhunting had become obvious, but indirect influences proved more complex and, in some cases, extremely convoluted. Pollution and the loss of living space are ultimately responsible for the declining populations of many species. Wide-ranging ramifications of those two problems have yet to be fully documented, and the pros and cons do not readily divide themselves into neat categories. Pesticides, the source of so many pollutants, also allow agriculture to be less risky and more productive, and human life to be more comfortable and healthier in a number of ways. Landscape transformations, in fact, may generate greater biological diversity as certain animals adapt readily to new conditions without much trouble, and some even thrive in disturbed environments.

Regardless of which side we take in the environmental debate, it is clearly important to understand the complex effects our actions have so that we do not find ourselves in a situation where our choices and opportunities are suddenly narrowed. Shortsightedness caused by lack of knowledge or motivated by immediate gain is no longer a justifiable excuse for the failure to maintain a healthy, nurturing environment. In the following pages we recount stories of six species that exemplify the spectrum of animals under review, the complexity of ecological issues involved in their rehabilitation, and the new regard for humbler or less prized creatures previously unrecognized.

The Houston Toad

In the late forties, John Wottring, an airplane mechanic and amateur herpetologist from southeast Houston, discovered near his home one night a number of small toads with a distinctive mating call. Wottring studied their behavior and showed them to professional herpetologists. Toads of the same kind were found in other scattered locations in southeast Texas. They were similar to the American toad (*Bufo americanus*), but in 1953 herpetologist Ottys Sanders declared them to be members of a distinct species, which he named *Bufo houstonensis*.

The Houston toad is smaller than its cousin the American toad. The male measures 2 to 2½ inches snout to vent (nose to tail), and the female measures 2¼ to 3¼ inches. Its back is light brown with

brown or black spots, each spot having one to three warts. A light stripe runs down the center of the back. The belly, chest, and throat are all cream-colored and usually mottled. Altogether it does not seem an outstanding creature, yet it gained some notoriety in the seventies as an example of the strange array of unknown plants and animals protected by the 1973 Endangered Species Act. The snail darter, which brought the construction of the Tellico Dam in Tennessee to a temporary halt, was the most famous of that group, but the Houston toad seemed the most laughable. A toad, after all, is not an object of great beauty or respect. It hops about wet, ghoulish places at night and is rumored in childhood folklore to give warts to those foolish enough to pick it up. A toad from Houston seems even more banal and ridiculous, a nondescript amphibian versus the booming Sunbelt sprawl.

After being officially named in 1953, the Houston toad slipped back into obscurity until the sixties, when University of Texas professor W. Frank Blair realized that the toad's numbers had rapidly declined. In 1965, graduate students came across a new population of Houston toads in Bastrop State Park, 110 miles northwest of Houston, but conditions indicated that it faced an uphill battle. The U.S. Fish and Wildlife Service officially listed the toad as endangered in 1970, and interest in it gained momentum. A recovery team, as provided for by the 1973 Endangered Species Act, began work in 1978. Also in 1978, the Fish and Wildlife Service designated critical habitat for the toad in Bastrop County, including Bastrop and Buescher State Parks and a large swath of surrounding private lands, and in Burleson County, where a much smaller population of toads survived. The service excluded proposed areas in Harris County around Houston. Extensive searches in the mid-seventies turned up only two toads in the area, and none have been seen since 1976. On two of the proposed sites, little or no suitable habitat remained. The service deemed the data insufficient to include four other proposed sites in the Houston area as critical habitat, to the immense relief of Houston developers, who were in the midst of an expansion frenzy fueled by skyrocketing oil profits.

The Houston toad exemplifies some of the problems involved in conserving endangered species that are not well known and that may exist only in extremely localized or isolated populations, as do many lower-order plants and animals. Several publications describe the toad as secretive, but its secretiveness lies mostly in the eyes of its would-be benefactors. In addition to existing only in small isolated populations (there are probably only 10,000 to 20,000 individuals), Houston toads burrow underground much of the time, and when they do emerge, it is usually at night around water: temporary rain pools or more-permanent drainage ditches, stock ponds, and lakes. All those factors make the animal a difficult subject for study.

The sudden interest in the little-known species sometimes resulted in the dissemination of preliminary findings as conclusive facts. It was reported, for example, that loblolly pines were a required element in the toad's habitat, an important consideration in defining and managing critical habitat. The recovery team's more comprehensive research shows that pine trees are not essential but that the toads do need sandy soil so their relatively weak legs can dig a burrow, where they spend the late summer and autumn months. The presence of pines, which thrive in sandy soil, is purely coincidental.

It was also widely believed that the toad emerged to breed early after the first warm rains of spring; in fact it now appears that they do so in late winter, regardless of rain, if the temperature has remained above 14°C (57°F) for the preceding 24 hours. That obviously becomes important when trying to monitor such an elusive species; an error in timing its appearance means lost data and dubious population estimates.

Finally, hybridization with other toads was reported to be the greatest threat to the survival of *Bufo houstonensis*. That conclusion was based on the suggestion in an early study that hybridization was a *potential* factor in the toad's decline. In fact, hybridization becomes important when habitat modification occurs, permitting other toads to move in.

The Houston toad may also be primarily a victim of gradual but comprehensive climatic changes that have taken place over millennia. Biologists believe that it and the similar American toad evolved from a common ancestor. When the last Ice Age ended, around 10,000 years ago, the area that is now Texas experienced an increase in temperature and a decrease in humidity. Fewer toads survived, and those that did became geographically and genetically isolated from cousins in the cooler, wetter north. Because of that restricted gene pool, *B. houstonensis* gradually developed into a distinct species, although research has recently considered whether *B. houstonensis* might actually be the same as *B. americanus charlesmithi*, found in Oklahoma and northcentral Texas. It appears to be a full species. Although the American toad adapts easily to a much greater range of habitats, the Houston toad's isolation and inbreeding have made it more specialized and less able to ride out even short-term climatic pulses. Its status as a relict of the Ice Age makes it an object of much interest but puts its long-range viability in some doubt. The severe drought that hit Texas during the fifties is believed to be largely responsible for the toad's decline. Water is an essential element in its habitat. Unlike other toads, it will breed readily even in temporary rain pools; indeed, rain pools were their typical breeding grounds until humans began altering drainage patterns for suburban and agricultural expansion.

Habitat loss represents the other threat to the Houston toad's continued existence. Around Houston, the loss has been devastating. The moist soil and pools of rainwater necessary for the toad are anathema to builders who need dry foundations for houses, offices, and roads. Lands are leveled, soils are drained, and entire drainage patterns are modified specifically to prevent the accumulation of standing water. Any water that is left is often polluted with pesticides and other contaminants (the effect of pesticide contamination on toads is just now coming under study). Dense development has also destroyed native vegetation in many areas, which in conjunction with pesticides affects the insect population on which the toad feeds. Even the soils themselves are attacked. The sandy soil in one area where Houston toads previously lived now lies beneath several inches of clay loam laid down for lawn and garden growth.

People have altered the Houston toad's habitat even in rural areas like Bastrop. In the sixties, the "lost pines" (western stands cut off from the Pineywoods) on private lands were being logged and cleared for houses and farms, but ironically the creation of two state parks also contributed to the toad's problems. The Parks and Wildlife Department leveled land for camping and picnic grounds and altered natural drainage patterns to create artificial lakes and stock ponds. Park policy changed direction in the seventies, and both parks are now managed to take into account the Houston toad and other animals and plants, although park authorities still face pressure to enlarge a golf course.

The recovery team now believes that the Bastrop population of Houston toads is in relatively good shape, provided that their habitat does not further deteriorate. The majority of the toads are on private lands, however, and as nearby Austin expands and its new airport goes in, those lands become increasingly valuable for development. The recovery program therefore emphasizes the necessity for involving local landowners in the campaign to protect the toad; not surprisingly, the landowners have shown little interest in saving the amphibian. Where there exists the possibility of federal intervention, many people fear that their interests will be sacrificed for those of the animal in question. The perception of conservation as being opposed to development remains one of the greatest obstacles in the path to a sound and healthy environment.

There is more to be discovered about the Houston toad. The Hermann Park Zoo in Houston is propagating toads in captivity for release in the wild and has reintroduced them in the Attwater's Prairie Chicken National Wildlife Refuge near Eagle Lake, but apparently without much success. Researchers are just beginning to accumulate baseline data, such as population numbers, trends, and habitat requirements. The search is also on for new populations that could possibly exist unknown to biologists and wildlife specialists. Saving the Houston toad will no doubt prove to be a difficult and complex matter. Its seeming inscrutability also makes it special, however—a small Texas toad trying to survive in a changing world. *Bufo houstonensis* may be a bit laughable, but it is not insignificant. Its consideration helps us to understand more deeply the minute and tangled webs that form our home.

The Red-Cockaded Woodpecker

In isolated pockets of east Texas pinelands, the red-cockaded woodpecker (*Picoides borealis*) lives in quiet but gravely threatened seclusion. Once ranging throughout the southeastern pine forests from Virginia south to Florida and west to Texas, this modest-sized bird, a little smaller than the ubiquitous northern cardinal, has become a prime example of the indirect effects that human activities have on wildlife. Unlike its much larger relative the ivory-billed woodpecker, the red-cockaded woodpecker was neither sought out as a prized trophy nor considered a pest. Similar in appearance to its more common cousins the downy woodpecker and the hairy woodpecker, but lacking their white vertical bars on the back, the red-cockaded woodpecker is relatively drab and inconspicuous, with what Peterson's Field Guide terms "zebra-backed," or horizontal white back stripes. Its red cockade is in reality only a minute red streak above the male's cheek, difficult to see even with good binoculars. In the dense longleaf pine forests where it made its home, the bird thus drew little notice. But those same forests provide southern mills with pulp and timber, and though millions of acres of pine stands remain, the particular habitat necessary for this highly specialized woodpecker is becoming an increasingly rare and, unfortunately, not very valuable commodity.

Although the bird's appearance is unremarkable, the red-cockaded's habitat preferences and behavior set it apart. Other woodpeckers excavate nests in the dry, easily worked wood of dead trees, but the red-cockaded selects only living pines for its home. Most birds that excavate tree cavities avoid live wood because its resin can foul their feathers, reducing their protective capacity. But the red-

Red-Cockaded Woodpecker

cockaded seems to welcome the resin, for in addition to drilling the main nest cavity, it removes the outer bark near the cavity and drills several adjacent holes. Abundantly flowing resin coats the area around the nest hole and oozes down the tree like wax from a burning candle, a good field sign of the woodpecker's presence. The resin coating may help the bird locate its nest cavity and act as a marker to warn off competing red-cockaded woodpeckers. Several observers also report that the resin foils predaceous invertebrates and tree-climbing snakes intent on finding a meal.

The toughness of living wood is another deterrent to woodpeckers, particularly to small ones like the red-cockaded. This species appears to overcome the obstacle by selecting pine trees at least 60 years old, and preferably 90 years to more than 100 years old. The older pines are often host to a fungus called red-heart, which softens the core-wood and makes excavation easier. Although some cavities have been found in healthy trees, most are located in pines with red-heart disease. Older trees also have a smaller volume of sapwood, so excess resin is less likely to flow into the nesting or roosting cavity and make it uninhabitable.

Today, the prime factor in the red-cockaded woodpecker's decline is the loss of suitable habitat, both in quantity and quality. More and more of the Southeast's pine forests are being leveled. In woods that remain, the older conifers preferred by the woodpecker are less valuable than younger trees. Today's foresters aim at producing wood as quickly as possible and so prefer rotation periods of 30 years or less before felling trees for pulp, and no longer than 50 years for other wood products. Old trees waste time, money, and space.

Real estate development also leads to habitat destruction. Where red-cockaded woodpeckers are known to live, developers using any type of federal money must set aside areas to be left intact for the birds. Some developers have attempted to get around the regulations. In Florida, a U.S. district court convicted two developers of killing red-cockaded woodpeckers. The men, upon discovering that land where they intended to build a subdivision was home to the endangered species, ordered employees to cut down trees with nest holes characteristic of the species and hunted down the birds themselves with shotguns. In a plea bargain, the developers received a two-year probation period and a $1,000 fine and agreed to contribute $300,000 to the National Fish and Wildlife Foundation.

The invasion of pine forests by hardwood species also adds to habitat deterioration. Lightning and fires started by Indians maintained the successional stage of parklike pinewoods before European settlement, but subsequent efforts of landowners to prevent and suppress fires have allowed hardwoods to establish themselves and crowd out pines. Even where pines remain, the red-cockaded woodpecker will not nest if there is a dense hardwood midstory around potential cavity trees. In addition to nest trees, the bird also needs a suitable foraging area of at least 25 acres, according to Texas researchers, and preferably around 100 acres. Preserving individual old pines here and there will not significantly contribute to the red-cockaded's survival. Finally, the isolation of remaining populations from one another threatens to reduce gene flow and impair the species' ability to expand and occupy new areas. Unfortunately, like wire grass, another member of the longleaf pine landscape, red-cockaded woodpeckers have not been documented to colonize a site from which they have been eliminated.

The Texas Parks and Wildlife Department initiated red-cockaded woodpecker studies in 1968, which led to the placement of the bird on the Red Data Book's list of rare and endangered species and the U.S. government's list in 1970. A recovery team was later appointed for the woodpecker in accordance with the provisions of the 1973 Endangered Species Act. The recovery team's recommendations clarified the need to protect existing cavity trees and to provide adequate foraging space, suitable trees for new cavities, and potential areas for future colonies pending an increase in the red-cockaded's population. Currently, there are about 225 active colonies in Texas. Those recommendations mean that the selective cutting of trees must replace the clear-cutting of whole tracts. In addition, the control of hardwoods on colony sites is absolutely vital, prescribed burning being the most effective method of control. Finally, the team recommended a 100-year rotational period for longleaf pines and 80-year rotations for other species. Private landowners are in no way bound by the recommendations, however, so the burden of implementation falls squarely on federal forestry managers. With proper management, biologists believe, both forestry and the woodpecker can prosper—a reminder that man and nature need not invariably be at odds.

Golden-Cheeked Warbler

THE GOLDEN-CHEEKED WARBLER

Between early March and early July, the rugged hills and valleys of central Texas play host to a rare and beautiful bird known as the golden-cheeked warbler (*Dendroica chrysoparia*). The small warbler has grown to be a favorite with local bird-watchers, especially since the sixties; it is found nowhere else in the United States, and it is the only bird that nests exclusively in Texas (although two inexplicable sightings have been reported elsewhere, one in Florida and another on the Farallon Islands off San Francisco, California). The U.S. Fish and Wildlife Service is currently reviewing the golden-cheeked warbler's status to determine if the bird should be added to its list of threatened and endangered species.

The golden-cheeked warbler is a member of the family of New World wood warblers, the Parulidae, termed the butterflies of the bird world, and, like other members, is distinctively and handsomely colored. The male's black crown, back, neck, and upper breast contrast vividly with its golden yellow cheeks, through which a black stripe extends back from the eyes. His wings are mostly black with white wingbars, complemented by a black tail with white outer feathers. The breast and belly are white. The female and young are less boldly colored, their cheeks a duller yellow and their backs, crowns, and wings largely olive-green.

Golden-cheeked warblers winter in the mountains of east-central Guatemala, Honduras, and Nicaragua, and it was in Guatemala that a British naturalist shot and collected the first two specimens in 1859. Toward the end of winter, the warblers make their way through the Sierra Madre Oriental of Mexico, finally arriving in their Texas nesting grounds during the first two weeks of March. Little is known about the bird in its winter range, and there is still much to learn about its life history in Texas.

What is clear is that its survival depends on dense stands of Ashe junipers, commonly known in Texas as cedar (though not a true cedar). The golden-cheeked warbler nests exclusively in juniper and oak woodlands, and the female uses long strips of juniper bark as a primary nest material. It cannot or will not use the bark of younger trees, which are more widespread in central Texas, but only that of junipers thirty years old or more, found in compact stands on the steep slopes and plateaus of the Hill Country and adjacent counties. Although it may feed in other trees, the species favors mixed stands of oaks and junipers for the abundance and diversity of insects they harbor. Mature Ashe junipers represent the primary limiting factor for the warbler's survival.

Mature cedar brakes are rapidly disappearing from the Hill Country of the eastern Edwards Plateau. The greatest destruction is taking place in Bexar, Kerr, and Travis counties where urban and suburban expansion is devouring land at an alarming rate. In Dallas County, the warbler is already history, the last small population having lost its nesting grounds in 1965. In rural areas, a cedar eradication program, begun in 1948 to convert cedar brakes to grasslands for livestock, has also contributed to habitat loss. Soil erosion is extensive in many of the cleared areas; in others secondary growth of brush-size cedars and oaks has occurred, but they are often not tall or dense enough to attract warblers.

Fortunately, the picture is brighter for the golden-cheeked warbler than for many species. The lands on which it makes its nests are economically most suitable for cattle, sheep, and goats. Sheep and goat grazing, when properly managed, is compatible with the golden-cheeked warbler's continued survival, as are deer hunting, limited juniper clearance, and certain forms of outdoor recreation, all of which can provide income to Hill Country residents. Proper management means preserving the older mixed stands of junipers and various oaks that blanket the plateaus and scarps of the eastern Edwards Plateau. Cedar brakes of up to several hundred acres are preferable, a thousand acres or more in a stand is ideal.

In 1966, the Travis County chapter of the Audubon Society acquired 94 acres of land 20 miles northwest of Austin and established it as the first sanctuary specifically for the golden-cheeked warbler. The original tract, now considerably enlarged in area, boasted approximately ten pairs. Male birds are relatively easy to spot as they establish territories by singing a raspy *lazee-daysee* song from the top of an oak, cedar elm, or other prominent tree around the junipers. At least 33 other bird species breed on the Audubon Sanctuary, but none appear as striking or ebullient as the goldencheek, wings quivering and head up in his song. The male's yellow cheek is even more striking as it catches the sun amid yellow-green spangles of oak pollen, hanging like miniature chandeliers around him on a late March morning.

Texas Parks and Wildlife Department is currently working on a management plan in Meridian State Park to study, develop, and improve habitat for the goldencheek. One major focus of research centers on how currently unusable cedar brakes might be made more attractive to the bird. If this small North American warbler goes on the U.S. list of endangered species (it has not as of April 1989), then more research, including studies of cowbird parasitism of its nests, a problem in fledging success, will be forthcoming. The brown-headed cowbird, *Molothrus ater*, may be a greater threat than researchers originally suspected.

THE OCELOT

Habitat destruction is also largely responsible for the current predicament of the ocelot (*Felis pardalis*), found on the state and federal lists of endangered species. The small cat survives in what's left of the thick brushlands in south Texas. But Mike Tewes, biologist at Texas A&I University's Caesar Kleberg Wildlife Research Institute in Kingsville, estimates that less than 1 percent of south Texas, stronghold for perhaps 80 to 120 animals, has the dense brush at ground level to support them. Such thick vegetation on fertile soils has been cleared extensively in previous decades to pasture livestock and, particularly in the lower Rio Grande Valley, to make way for citrus, cotton, and other cash crops.

Linnaeus first named the ocelot in 1758, but to this day little is known about the animal. The male's average length, from nose to tail tip, is around 45 inches (its long tail by itself measures around 15 inches), and it weighs between 15 and 25 pounds, about the size of a bobcat. The female is slightly smaller. No two ocelots have the same markings. The ocelot's ground color ranges from whitish or tawny yellow to reddish gray, and its darker spots come in several sizes and shapes, mostly elongate forms linked together to give an almost striped appearance.

Unlike some larger cats, the ocelot poses no danger to livestock, preferring to hunt small mammals, such as rabbits and rats, and ground-dwelling birds in a home range of about 15 square kilometers. Nevertheless, efforts to control livestock predators have taken a toll on the small cat. The killing of hundreds of thousands of ocelots for fashionable fur has also decimated the cat's population in Central and South America, where it was once abundant in jungles, forests, and thick brush as far south as Uruguay and northern Argentina.

Although it formerly ranged north onto the Edwards Plateau, the ocelot was never as common in Texas as it was farther south, and the fur trade rarely bothered itself with Texas ocelots. When the cat was listed as endangered in 1972, an oversight caused the U.S. population

Ocelot

to be excluded from the listing, a situation corrected in 1982. In any event, Texas was already protecting the ocelot, and it is here that a wide-ranging research project has been under way to understand the ecology and life history of the little-known feline and to assess prospects for relocation, including habitat corridors that enable cats to disperse.

Because the ocelot is largely nocturnal and almost never shows itself in open country, it is an extremely difficult animal to study. In 1981, Mike Tewes and other researchers at the Kleberg Institute began trapping ocelots and fitting them with collars carrying radio transmitters. So far, 40 different ocelots have been trapped a total of 85 times; one female first taken in 1982 was still alive in December 1988. Preliminary results have clearly demonstrated the ocelot's need for thick, nearly impenetrable brush. Kleberg biologists discovered their first ocelot den in the fall of 1985 on Laguna Atascosa National Wildlife Refuge. It was a mere barren depression in the earth amid a dense thorn thicket. Ocelot habitat preferences, so unlike those of bobcats, who live on the edges of thickets, and of mountain lions, who range widely through varying vegetation, are doubtless at the root of the ocelot's problems. Areas of thick brush indicate relatively good soils and are among the first to be cleared for crops. The ocelot does not adjust well to cleared land.

Other findings from radio telemetry indicate that a previously unrecognized factor—road kills—may also adversely affect survival, notably in suboptimal habitat into which younger animals may stray. At least six ocelots have been struck by traffic in recent years. In March 1988, a male and two females were moved within Laguna Atascosa Refuge away from a heavily traveled area to minimize the risk of being hit by vehicles. One of the females remained close to the release site; the radiotagged male moved away but remained on the refuge, and the other female moved back the few miles to her original range.

At present, Laguna Atascosa and other portions of Cameron County and adjacent Willacy County are the center of ocelot research in the U.S. About twenty thousand acres are currently being managed specifically for the cat's survival; whether that is adequate to maintain the population will become clearer as more information is gathered. The ocelot also occurs on private land in south Texas, some of which is leased for deer hunting compatible with ocelot survival. The U.S. Fish and Wildlife Service is acquiring parcels of land along the Rio Grande to create a corridor through which wildlife, including the ocelot and its endangered cat cousin, the jaguarundi, can roam and expand their range. With that corridor intact and revegetated with native plants, itself a herculean task, and with the translocation of cats to presently unused habitat in south and southcentral Texas, biologists hope that *Felis pardalis* will maintain and strengthen its fragile foothold in the United States.

POISONS IN THE FOOD CHAIN:
The Bald Eagle and the Peregrine Falcon

The Houston toad, red-cockaded woodpecker, golden-cheeked warbler, and ocelot all have narrow and specialized habitat needs that explain their current predicaments. But specialized animals are not the only ones to suffer the ill effects of life in the modern world. Other more adaptive creatures have also fallen victim to human tampering with the invisible links and pathways that make up local environments and the global ecosystem. The bald eagle and peregrine falcon are examples of generalists—animals that are able to take advantage of a relatively broad range of resources—whose numbers have dropped to dangerously low levels in the twentieth century. Habitat loss, hunting, and, in the case of the peregrine, egg and bird collecting have contributed to their decline, but the critical factor has been their position high in the food chain.

The eagle has been a symbol of power for centuries. Native Americans believed that wearing eagle feathers endowed them with strength and swiftness. In 1782, the newly formed government of the United States, still fighting for independence, adopted the bald eagle, the only eagle whose distribution is restricted to North America, as its national emblem. Despite Benjamin Franklin's objections that the bird was lazy, cowardly, and of bad moral character, the bald eagle remains a proud symbol of freedom for many contemporary Americans. Yet as early as 1940, eagle numbers had declined to the point that the U.S. Congress passed a law making it illegal to harm the bird. Declines continued, however, and by 1970, the bald eagle faced extinction in many parts of its range, including Texas.

Bald Eagle

Despite its special status, many people concur with Ben Franklin's opinion and consider both the bald eagle and the golden eagle, North America's two eagle species, enemies of man. Stories abound of eagles attacking and carrying off livestock, particularly sheep, and even human babies, although an eagle, which weighs eight to fourteen pounds on average, cannot possibly carry away anything as heavy or heavier than itself. There are documented cases of the powerful birds preying on lambs and kids, which have earned both North American eagles enmity from sheep and goat raisers. Ingrained prejudices against the eagle also reflect another side of our national emblem. The bald eagle is indeed an opportunist and a scavenger. Fish is a preferred food, and though it will hunt for itself, it will also steal fish caught by other birds of prey such as ospreys. Where fish aren't readily available, it will prey on diseased or injured waterfowl, often feasting on ducks and geese wounded by hunters. Eagles, particularly golden eagles, can also sometimes be seen on fences and telephone poles waiting, it seems, for passing automobiles to run over rabbits and other rodents.

Many generalist species, because they are not limited to a narrow range of resources, have little trouble maintaining and even increasing their numbers. The reasons for the bald eagle's decline are numerous and complex. Many birds were routinely shot as pests, and despite federal protection, shooting is still a leading cause of premature death among juveniles and adults. Donald G. Schueler's *Incident at Eagle Ranch* reports the deaths of more than one hundred bald and golden eagles from aerial gunning in Real County in the winters of 1975–76 and 1976–77. Poisons set out for predator and rodent control on ranch and agricultural lands have also contributed to eagle deaths.

The bald eagle's difficulties, however, ran deeper than the deaths of individual birds, serious as those were. The major factor in the bird's decline appeared to be lowered reproductive success; that is, the number of young reared per pair was decreasing, and some pairs were producing no young at all. A 1964 study in Alaska, where the eagle population is relatively healthy, showed an average of one fledgling per nest, but in 1973 bald eagle pairs averaged only 0.14 fledglings per nest in the Great Lakes region. Habitat loss has contributed to declining productivity, especially the loss of nest sites. Eagles nest in large, usually old, trees, often within half a mile of a river, stream, or lake. Suburban and agricultural expansion, clearing, and removal of mature trees have destroyed nest sites across the nation, even in remote areas that would otherwise be suitable. In some areas, the pollution and siltation of rivers and lakes has destroyed fish populations, the primary food in the bald eagle's diet. But the real villain behind the eagle's lowered productivity was more troublesome and more frightening. The eagle, like the peregrine falcon and other birds of prey, had fallen victim to man's obsession with pesticides, particularly chlorinated hydrocarbons. The most popular and now most infamous was DDT. Although DDT rarely killed birds directly, once ingested it was metabolized into DDE, which, among other things, inhibits the production of enough calcium to form a sturdy eggshell to protect the embryo. Eggs broke easily, or their embryos developed abnormally and never hatched. The bald eagle's diet of fish and waterfowl in areas where pesticides were sprayed or into which they had drained made this carnivorous species especially susceptible because the concentration of the chemical is magnified as it moves up the food chain.

The bald eagle is divided into two subspecies, the southern (*Haliaeetus leucocephalus leucocephalus*) and the northern (*H. l. alascanus*). The only physical difference is the slightly larger size of the northern subspecies, which breeds in Alaska, Canada, and across the northern tier of the continental United States, as far south as Oregon in the west and Maryland in the east. The southern subspecies breeds mostly in wetlands along the lower Mississippi, the coasts of the Atlantic and Gulf of Mexico from New Jersey to Texas, the coast of California and Baja California, and in Arizona and New Mexico. Both subspecies occur in Texas from late fall through early spring. In 1988, enthusiasts counted 143 eagles at 13 sites in Texas, substantially above the average of about 80 for wintering birds. The northern race winters around large bodies of water, mostly in east Texas and the Panhandle, particularly near Buffalo Lake, Lake Meredith, and Palo Duro Canyon. Smaller numbers of the southern race nest along the Texas Gulf Coast.

The Department of Interior listed the southern bald eagle as endangered in 1967. In 1978, the government declared both subspecies to be endangered in 43 of the 48 continental United States, including Texas, and threatened in the remaining 5. Only in Alaska did the eagle population enjoy relative health. Five regional recovery teams were established to develop plans and programs to stabilize eagle numbers. In 1972, President Nixon issued a ban on the general use of DDT, and that, along with more-informed management practices, has helped to halt the eagle's decline. Numbers of nesting eagles are on the rise in most places, and researchers involved with the captive-breeding program at the Patuxent Wildlife Research Center near Laurel, Maryland, are working to reintroduce the species to areas where it has disappeared.

The Texas Parks and Wildlife Department is actively involved in studying and protecting the state's bald eagle population, particularly the small group of southern bald eagles that nest along the Gulf Coast. The birds arrive in Texas during August and September, lay their eggs in November, and depart between April and June. Where they go then remains unclear. Parks and Wildlife began eagle-nest surveys in 1971 to determine how many remained and what their reproductive trends looked like. At that time only 5 nests were known to exist, although more surely went undiscovered. By 1985, though, 28 nests had been discovered, 17 of which were in active use.

In 1987 there were 17 active nests on the coastal prairie between Rockport and Houston, and an additional 2 active nests in southeast Texas. Between 1971 and 1985, 130 bald eagles fledged in Texas, a significant increase considering that in 1974 biologists estimated that there were only 150 to 250 bald eagles in the entire state and that over 80 percent were probably nonnesting members of the northern race.

Parks and Wildlife began a new program in spring 1985 to band some eagles to gauge their survival rate and to determine where they go after nesting. So far, more than fifty young eagles have been banded, and surprisingly, sightings have come from as far north as Montana and Canada.

Like the eagle, the falcon has long been a symbol of power in human cultures. The ancient Egyptian god Horus, meaning "the lofty one," ruled over the sun and sky and took the form of a falcon. Farther east, in the steppes of Central Asia, nomadic tribesmen developed the practice or, as many would say, the art of falconry—the use of falcons, eagles, and hawks to hunt down other birds and mammals. Attila the Hun (A.D. 406–453) may have introduced the sport into Europe, where the bird of preference for kings and noblemen was the peregrine falcon, revered for its speed, strength, and phenomenal agility in the air.

The peregrine falcon (*Falco peregrinus*) graces the skies over every continent save Antarctica, though its actual numbers have always been relatively low compared with other birds. Three subspecies inhabit North America: the Arctic peregrine (*F. p. tundrius*), found from northern Alaska across the Canadian tundra; the American peregrine (*F. p. anatum*), found throughout northern Mexico, the continental U.S., and into southern portions of Alaska and Canada; and Peale's peregrine (*F. p. pealei*), a resident of the coast of British Columbia and southern Alaska. The size of a crow, the peregrine is slate gray or blue above, its underparts white to buff and extensively spotted and barred. Its head is also dark, with black mustache marks on each cheek. Like other falcons, the peregrine sports a long tail and long, pointed wings, giving it a triangular silhouette in flight.

The peregrine's status as an uncommon bird no doubt adds to its mystique, as does its preference for nesting on the ledges of cliffs and other high places from which it can survey its surrounding territory,

Peregrine Falcon

hence its loftiness in human eyes. Its diet consists mainly of birds, ranging in size from waterfowl (earning it the name "duck hawk") down to small passerines, or perching birds, such as sparrows and warblers. It stoops (dives) down on its prey from above, at speeds at times in excess of 200 miles per hour, grasping smaller birds in its claws or knocking down larger ones with a violent, raking blow that often stuns or kills them. It may come swooping down from out of the sun or give chase by following every twist and turn of its quarry. Pairs often hunt together; one flushes a bird while the other circles above, ready to launch a deadly dive.

The peregrine, notably the tundra race, often nests on cliffs along seacoasts, rivers, and lakes where large numbers of waterfowl and shorebirds feed. But it is no stranger to man; ledges on tall buildings in modern cities also provide suitable nesting sites. Cities are often homes for tens of thousands of pigeons, easy and tasty prey for the falcon, who encounters far fewer threats in urban areas from traditional enemies like larger raptors and owls. A highly adaptable species, the peregrine has survived falconers, hunters, and other humans for centuries. Its presence in North America dates back at least 30,000 years to the Pleistocene, when it bred nearly everywhere on the continent. As the glaciers receded, higher temperatures and decreased precipitation may have caused a gradual decrease in the peregrine population. Despite its reported decline, historic records suggest that peregrines remained well distributed in the northern hemisphere until recent times.

In the late fifties, however, the peregrine population began to crash. Rumors in 1962 that no young peregrines had fledged in the northeastern United States were sadly confirmed in 1964 when a survey of 133 traditional aeries found not a single nesting bird. Altogether there had once been around 300 known occupied aeries in the eastern United States and southeast Canada, but by the mid-sixties the eastern race of peregrines was extinct. In the western U.S., the peregrine survived, but just barely. One hundred and eighty pairs of peregrines were known to have bred in the region encompassing the Rocky Mountains, the Southwest, and the Great Plains; the recovery team appointed for that region reported that fewer than thirty pairs remained in 1976. In California, a hundred pairs were reproducing successfully in 1946, but the number had dropped to five by 1970. The tundra subspecies was also experiencing a population drop in most areas, though not to the same degree as the American peregrine. Both the *tundrius* and *anatum* subspecies were listed as endangered in 1970. The only other peregrine race in North America, Peale's peregrine, seemed to be holding its own and was not listed.

The culprit behind the peregrine's near extinction was, as for the bald eagle, chlorinated hydrocarbon pesticides. In Massachusetts, broken eggshells were found in aeries as early as 1947. The story was the same everywhere, although the degree of damage varied depending on the concentration of pesticide residues in bird prey. Reproductive success plummeted, and the few falcons that actually produced young were unable to maintain the population. High levels of DDE in adult peregrines also caused abnormal parental behavior, such as nest desertion, abandonment of eggs and nestlings, and even consumption of their own eggs by female falcons.

Indiscriminate shooting, habitat disturbance and loss, and collecting of the birds for falconry have also been factors in the peregrine's decline. Trapping peregrine falcons became illegal in 1970, when the species was listed as endangered.

But the story of the peregrine did not end there. The federal government's ban on the use of DDT helped to end hard pesticide accumulation (although DDE continues to be found in the birds and their eggs, probably from illegal spraying of DDT in the U.S. and from its still legal use in Central and South America). But experts felt more could be done to buttress the dwindling population in the West and reintroduce the species in the East, where, many ornithologists believe, the gene pool for the *anatum* subspecies is extinct. It was in that effort that the knowledge and expertise of falconers, some of whom had been among the first to express alarm over the peregrine's decline, played an indispensable role. In the forefront of what became a successful captive-breeding and reintroduction program stood Tom Cade, a Cornell University ornithologist. Cade established the Peregrine Fund in 1970 and began to produce offspring from captive birds in 1973 with the intention of releasing them into the wild (accomplished successfully in 1975). Biologists bred falcons that originated from North and South America, Spain, the United Kingdom, and even Australia. After ten years of hard work breeding the falcon and developing hacking techniques whereby captive-bred birds could be successfully released in the wild, Cade found that two pairs of freed peregrines had produced four young in their New Jersey release areas. That event in 1980 represented the first time peregrines had successfully fledged young in the eastern U.S. in nearly twenty years and crowned Cade's efforts to bring peregrines back as wild birds. Similar breeding programs began operating in Canada, Colorado, New Mexico, and Pennsylvania, and peregrines have been released in a number of places, including west Texas. Cade has attributed the success of those captive-breeding programs "largely to the fact that we had the accumulated technology developed by falconers over the centuries that was ready-made for our purpose." Additional methods of helping peregrines included cross-fostering them with the more abundant western cousin, the prairie falcon, which has incubated peregrine eggs and raised young as its own.

Both the American and the Arctic peregrines have historically occurred in Texas. The Arctic race passes through from March through May on migration to arctic breeding sites and again from August through October on its journey south to wintering grounds in South America. A prime way station is South Padre Island, whose beaches and wetlands attract shorebirds and ducks, the peregrine's common prey. The barrier island is thus an important spot for ornithologists interested in tracking the bird and estimating population numbers and trends. The more sedentary American race currently breeds in the Trans-Pecos region, though it once resided in central Texas as well (the last confirmed record of breeding on the Edwards Plateau was in Kerr County in 1908). The Chihuahuan Desert, stretching into west Texas, was one of the last places in the U.S. where peregrine falcons continued to breed in the sixties and seventies, and it remains a primary focus of attention for state and federal wildlife officials. The known nesting sites or aeries, to which birds remain faithful year after year, are being carefully monitored, and the production of young seems to be finally on the upswing, although hydrocarbon levels in the birds are still higher than expected. Nesting peregrines in Big Bend National Park are also vulnerable to hikers and rock climbers, who, like the peregrine, seem to head invariably for the highest sites, the bird to raise its young and humans for the view. The falcon will desert its nest if humans cause too much disturbance.

Falconers and conservationists aren't the only people interested in the peregrine falcon. Because of its high position on the food chain and its worldwide distribution, the falcon is a good global indicator of the environment's biological health. Researchers at the University of Texas System Cancer Center are putting it to use in cancer studies. Where falconers once combed the sands of South Padre Island looking for birds to trap, scientists now set out pigeon lures to snare the falcons for blood samples. In those samples, they can find the whole spectrum of chemicals people have sprayed on their fields, ranches, and lawns and study more closely the dynamics of pollution biology.

Peregrine falcon numbers are on the rebound. The Arctic subspecies has increased its numbers by such a margin that in 1984 the U.S. Fish and Wildlife Service lowered its status to the threatened category. Nesting American peregrines south of Canada remain in low numbers, with probably no more than 10 percent of their aboriginal population surviving, but recovery has at least gotten under way. The proud peregrine may yet command the awe and admiration of human generations to come.

6 THIRSTY TEXAS: Development and Endangered Water Life

The conflict between economic development and the survival of various animals has colored conservation efforts for many years. The battle becomes more heated and complex as the species become more obscure, the Houston toad being a case in point. Aquatic and other water-dependent species tend to be some of the most obscure and least appreciated creatures. Wet, cold, scaly, and lacking the familiar traits of terrestrial animals, they evoke little concern among their human neighbors.

In Texas, economic prosperity has come largely from oil wealth, but the state's survival depends on another ultimately more valuable resource—water. The abundant rivers and creeks of east Texas provided sustenance to Indians and early settlers alike. Copious springs and rivers in the central part of the state made agriculture and later large-scale urbanization possible. The aquifers lying beneath the High Plains allowed much of the Panhandle to flourish as a center for irrigated cotton, sorghum, and wheat.

All of those achievements required and continue to demand massive drafts from the state's water supply. Large urban populations add pressure to dam more and more rivers, and as cities expand, engineers rechannel entire drainage basins, causing unseen perturbations for a variety of water-dependent organisms. Agricultural authorities do the same in an effort to obtain the maximum amount of water possible, while individual farmers and ranchers rearrange water supplies on their lands on a smaller scale. The pumping of groundwater from aquifers for cities and farms directly or indirectly supports several million people. Their depletion currently threatens a wide variety of plants and animals, and ultimately our own well-being will be at stake.

SPRING-ADAPTED FISHES:
The Clear Creek Gambusia and Pupfish of the Trans-Pecos

Interest in Texas fishes and their protection goes back to the 1870s. Joseph Dinkins, the first fish commissioner, reported to the Legislature on the poor condition of the state's freshwater fisheries. His concern focused on the useful (i.e., edible) species, and the response centered on conserving and improving that commercially valuable resource. Where native inhabitants of rivers, streams, and lakes proved insufficient, people introduced nonnative fishes like the common carp, *Cyptinus carpio*, to build up the stock of food fish, or they imported other species from out-of-state. More than a century later, fish are still regarded primarily as a commercial and recreational resource, and much effort goes into managing their production, regulating their take, and developing new and efficient ways to put them to use, as in the recent proposal to establish fish farms in west Texas.

There are, however, other species of fish swimming in Texas waters, generally unnoticed as they ply quiet spring-fed pools, creeks, and rivers. The only conceivable use for them might be as bait for something bigger. Yet many of these small fish can be said to be the truest of true Texans, having evolved and adapted over many millennia to the peculiarities of their local habitats. Of the eight federally listed endangered species of fish in Texas, all but one are endemic to the state. Ironically, their successful adjustment to local geography and hydrology may prove to be their downfall. As human inhabitants build, drill, and irrigate, transforming the landscape into an ecologically simplified commercial market, the first species to suffer are those that are most dependent on unique local ecosystems. These fish were denizens of a pristine Texas where springwaters gushed out of the

Clear Creek Gambusia

ground and rivers flowed unimpeded to the sea. Their continued existence is currently jeopardized because they depend on the one resource that we value even more than oil—fresh water. Water is being sucked up from around and beneath the creatures' homes to provide the lifeblood for farms, towns, and cities.

Nearly all of the federally listed endangered fish in Texas are associated with springs and spring-fed streams, lakes, or marshes. The springwaters emanate from underground reservoirs like the Edwards (Balcones Fault Zone) and Edwards-Trinity (Plateau) aquifers. In the Balcones Fault Zone, water deep under the earth makes its way to the surface along cracks or faults, creating spring systems like those in New Braunfels and San Marcos, the largest and second-largest springs in Texas, respectively. In west Texas, surface water penetrates into the earth until it encounters impervious clays, then flows horizontally to emerge eventually as a spring in a valley or streambed. The pumping of such groundwater has made life not only possible but prosperous in semiarid western lands. Even in central Texas, San Antonio and other cities depend on underground water for drinking and industrial supplies. Of the 281 major springs in Texas, however,

65 no longer exist, and many others cease flowing intermittently, with devastating consequences for their aquatic life. Other springs are inundated when rivers are dammed, drastically altering water temperature, flow, vegetation, and other environmental characteristics, making it impossible for certain species to survive. The Amistad (or Goodenough) gambusia (*Gambusia amistadensis*) and the Rio Grande bluntnose shiner (*Notropis simus simus*) were victims of the damming of the Rio Grande. The former disappeared after the completion of the Amistad Dam at Del Rio and is now believed to be extinct. The reservoir that formed behind the dam swallowed up nearby tributaries and springs, including Goodenough Spring, the third-largest in the state. The bluntnose shiner has not been seen for twenty years in Texas, although a subspecies was recently discovered in the New Mexico section of the Pecos River.

Perhaps the most remarkable aspect of endangered fishes is their extremely localized distribution and small and often fluctuating populations. Many are restricted to small, isolated drainage systems, and a few are found only in a single spring or system of springs. The Clear Creek gambusia (*Gambusia heterochir*) is an example of the latter. The problems faced by this gambusia are representative of those faced by spring fishes throughout the American West. *G. heterochir* grows to about two inches long and resembles the common guppy (they belong to the same family, Poeciliidae). In 1953, while sampling for the greenthroat darter in Wilkinson Springs on the Clear Creek Ranch near Menard, Texas, ichthyologists Clark Hubbs and Kirk Strawn discovered *G. heterochir* along with the mosquito fish (*Gambusia affinis*) and some hybrids. Hubbs first described the Clear Creek gambusia in 1957, and by 1967 it had already found its way to the federal endangered species list.

Clear Creek originates from a series of limestone springs associated with the Edwards-Trinity Aquifer, and at one time it flowed freely for just over three miles to its confluence with the San Saba River. The Wilkinson family established a ranch around the springs in 1878. Either they or someone before them built a low earth-and-concrete dam about 250 feet (75 meters) downstream from the headsprings to form a small pool of about one hectare. The Wilkinsons built their first home near the pool and used its water to irrigate fields downstream. During the thirties, three more dams were constructed so that Clear Creek became a series of impounded ponds. Spring-adapted fauna probably inhabited the entire length of the creek before the dams were built, but subsequent changes in habitat favored the invasion of eurythermal animals, that is, those tolerant of wide temperature fluctuations. Those hardier animals overwhelmed the spring-run fauna, which were used to the relatively constant temperatures of the flowing springs. At the present time, G. *heterochir* finds refuge only in the pool behind the first dam, where it is partially protected from competitors and where water temperatures are nearly constant. Conservation efforts therefore focus on the spring pool and on strengthening the dam to prevent the influx of harmful competitors, specifically mosquito fish.

The mosquito fish presents a threat to more-specialized spring fishes throughout the western United States. In many areas it was introduced for mosquito control; it now appears that at least some of the native fishes it replaces are equally good or better for that purpose. The mosquito fish tolerates a broader range of aquatic habitats than the Clear Creek gambusia and can reproduce in greater numbers, overwhelming native fish and the limited resources and conditions on which they depend. In addition, the mosquito fish, a gambusia itself, mates with some other species of its genus, including the Clear Creek gambusia. Because the offspring of such interspecific matings tend to possess hybrid vigor, they are likely to compete more successfully than their genetically pure parents and may eventually replace the original species.

The Wilkinson family played a major role in protecting the Clear Creek gambusia, a rare example of private landowners' becoming involved in the conservation of creatures that are of no discernible economic benefit. Through the years there have been several breaches in the dam, breaches that allowed migrating mosquito fish to enter the spring pool. The family helped keep the aging dam together by controlling the alien nutria that were undermining it and by removing shrubs and trees whose roots were breaking it apart. Finally in 1979, the Rio Grande Fishes Recovery Team shored up the dam with extensive repairs that have prevented mosquito fish ingress for the last decade.

After running the ranch for four generations, the Wilkinsons put it up for sale in 1982. Those concerned for the fish feared that new owners might develop the land for resort housing or otherwise use it in ways that would destroy or damage the all-important headspring pool. Fortunately, the new owners have shown similar conservation-oriented commitment and responsibility, keeping the Clear Creek gambusia in good hands for the time being. Larger threats of groundwater depletion and contamination are unfortunately beyond the control of even the most well-meaning landowners and wildlife agencies. In addition, the small population and extremely restricted geographical range of species like the Clear Creek gambusia mean that a single catastrophic event could wipe them out literally overnight. Similar threats hang over nearly all endangered aquatic organisms in Texas.

The U.S. Fish and Wildlife Service lists two species of pupfish as endangered in Texas, the Leon Springs pupfish (*Cyprinodon bovinus*) and the Comanche Springs pupfish (*Cyprinodon elegans*). Both appellations are ironic as neither one currently inhabits the spring for which it was named. Discovered in 1851, C. *bovinus* had disappeared from Leon Springs, west of Fort Stockton, at least by the forties, and probably earlier, as a result of the damming, diversion, and poisoning of the springwaters to rid them of introduced carp. The pupfish was thought to be extinct when in 1965 a new population was discovered in Diamond Y Springs and its outflow into Leon Creek, nine miles north of Fort Stockton. Although that population appears to be in fairly good condition, it too is extremely vulnerable to sudden catastrophic events. Active oil and gas fields surround the fish's habitat, and a refinery lies just 500 yards upstream from the main springhead. Oil spills have occurred with relative frequency, and some have killed pupfish. The oil company, landowners, and government biologists have taken concerted steps to prevent spills from reaching the headsprings, but the threat to the fish remains real. As in the case of the Clear Creek gambusia, introduced species pose another hazard to the Leon Springs pupfish. In this instance the villain is the sheepshead minnow (*Cyprinodon variegatus*), a Gulf species. The inadvertent introduction of the minnows into Leon Creek in 1974 led to widespread hybridization, which continued until the last of the minnows and hybrids were removed in August 1978. The Fish and Wildlife Service has designated the entire present range of the Leon Springs pupfish as critical habitat.

In 1849, a U.S. Cavalry captain marveled at Comanche Springs' "clear gush of water which bursts from the plain, unperceived until the traveler is immediately upon it . . . abounding in fish and soft-shell turtles." Settlers began using the springwater as early as 1875 to irrigate their lands, and by 1955 the large Pecos County spring, lying within the city limits of present-day Fort Stockton, had run dry, eliminating the fish, turtles, and other aquatic organisms that had once flourished there. The Comanche Springs pupfish, discovered in 1853 and one of the two most distinctive pupfishes in the United States, now survives only in a system of interconnected springs and irrigation canals near Balmorhea in Reeves County, 55 miles west of Fort Stockton. The area was mostly marshland before 1875, when local farmers began to construct canals to divert the springwater into their fields. The marshes dried up, and flow from the springs rapidly decreased, greatly reducing the pupfish's habitat and numbers. Sparse populations remain scattered through the canal system fed by Phantom Lake Spring and in Giffin and San Solomon springs.

Unlike other, more specialized endangered fish such as the Clear Creek gambusia, the Comanche Springs pupfish demonstrates a relatively broad range of ecological tolerance. Although it feeds primarily on the bottom of canals, marshes, and creeks, it can feed at the surface and other levels. It breeds throughout most of the year, and spawning can occur in flowing or stagnant water. Springhead waters of constant temperature and waters of more varying temperature in pools and channels downstream appear to be equally acceptable to the pupfish. Unfortunately, that same broadness of ecological needs makes almost any other fish a potential competitor. A large variety of fishes occur in the same habitat, and other *Cyprinodon* species, like the sheepshead minnow, pose special threats. Fishermen possibly introduced the minnow into Lake Balmorhea when, after a day's fishing, they dumped their bait buckets with the unused, commercially grown minnows into the lake. Hybridization is occurring between the two species where they coexist, in part because the Comanche Springs pupfish does not perform the elaborate prespawning rituals that usually prevent one fish species from mating with another and because it lacks any distinct preference for a particular breeding habitat.

Phantom Lake Spring will probably run dry within fifty years, and as more water is pumped from the Edwards-Trinity Aquifer, the entire Balmorhea spring system will one day cease flowing. In 1974, the

Texas Parks and Wildlife Department constructed a small refugium in the Balmorhea State Recreation Area that provides a stable and secure habitat for several thousand Comanche Springs pupfish for the time being. The long-term survival of the pupfish may depend on captive breeding. The U.S. Fish and Wildlife Service is propagating a growing population of the fish at the Dexter National Fish Hatchery in New Mexico, for research purposes and for potential reintroduction should some disaster befall the wild population. The Comanche Springs pupfish joins several other endangered species of fish at Dexter, whose captive stocks may represent the last best hope for those creatures.

BLINDCATS AND WATER SNAKES

Not only are there fish dependent on clean and plentiful springwaters flowing out of aquifers but there are also fish living deep in subterranean cavities of the aquifers themselves. Of the 40 species of North American catfish (family Ictaluridae), 3 live underground: one in an aquifer beneath Coahuila, Mexico, and two in the Edwards Aquifer near San Antonio. Information about them is woefully lacking, largely because their habitats are so inaccessible. The only specimens available are those that are periodically forced to the surface of the artesian wells in which they live.

Because they live in a dark troglodytic world, the catfish have no use for eyes, hence their common name "blindcat." The various colors that distinguish other fish are likewise useless, and the blindcats, like many other subterranean creatures, are a uniform white. The Texas blindcats inhabit what is known as the San Antonio Pool, a section of the Edwards Aquifer penetrated by five artesian wells. In three of the wells, both species of blindcat, the widemouth (*Satan eurystomus*) and the toothless (*Trogloglanis pattersoni*), live together, while each fish has one of the remaining two wells to itself. Biologists do not know precisely why the blindcats inhabit some places and not others, but temperature appears to be important. The five wells in the San Antonio Pool average 80°F, eight degrees warmer than other nearby wells in which no blindcats swim. Their life history and diet are likewise puzzles. The toothless blindcat is the most highly specialized catfish known. Lacking teeth, it has a uniquely convoluted digestive system. It is most likely a herbivore, feeding on detritus and fungal growth. The widemouth is known to be a carnivore and preys on blind shrimp, amphipods, and, where they exist together, on its toothless cousin.

Although the Mexican blindcat is on the federal list of endangered species, the situation of the widemouth and toothless blindcats is not currently seen as critical. Nonetheless, a combination of potential threats has moved the Texas Parks and Wildlife Department to put both fish on its own list of protected nongame species, the state's equivalent of the federal threatened category. Predicted lower levels of groundwater in the San Antonio Pool will adversely affect the blindcats' food supply and its ability to reproduce, while contamination of the aquifer by pesticides and other chemical pollutants could make what water remains uninhabitable.

Fish are not the only aquatic creatures to suffer from human alteration of riparian habitats, pollution, and groundwater depletion. Residents of west-central Texas are now only too familiar with the Concho water snake (*Nerodia harteri paucimaculata*), a nonvenomous denizen of the Colorado and Concho rivers. Formerly ranging over 276 miles of those two rivers, it has disappeared from 78 miles of upstream habitat and occurs only in scattered sections of the remainder. The main factor in the snake's decline appears to be the construction of various impoundments that have altered the character of the riparian habitat. The Concho water snake is particularly susceptible to those changes because juveniles of the species live and feed in shallow, fast-flowing riffles with rocky substrates. Damming eliminates the riffle areas above the dam and can cause the riverbed below the dam to become clogged with silt. The construction of Stacy Reservoir on the Colorado River near the Concho-Coleman county line will inundate more than half of that primary habitat and also affect the area downstream.

The Texas Parks and Wildlife Code lists the Concho water snake as endangered and a related subspecies, the Brazos water snake (*Nerodia harteri harteri*), as threatened. Although state law prohibits the collection, possession, and sale of endangered animals without a permit, it contains no provisions for habitat preservation. The federal law does, however, so when the Fish and Wildlife Service recently listed the Concho subspecies as threatened, its action caused a major controversy, coinciding with the initial phases of the Stacy Reservoir project, a $68 million enterprise designed to provide 100 million gallons of water a day to west Texas. National environmental organiza-

Concho Water Snake

tions charged that Texas interests were holding up the 1986 reauthorization bill for the Endangered Species Act. A Texas congressman tried and failed to get the water snake deleted from the threatened species list.

Construction of the waterworks finally proceeded in tandem with a long-term research project examining the snake's ecology, but the conflict left bitter feelings. Local residents, who say the reservoir is crucial to their economic well-being, deeply resented that a snake's survival was given, as they saw it, higher priority than their own. The conflict demonstrated once again the need for deeper thinking and a fuller understanding of human and animal communities so that the issue does not revolve around snakes-versus-people but rather around how we can work toward our goals in less damaging ways.

Conserving Riparian Systems

Because so many endangered or threatened species in Texas suffer primarily from habitat modification and loss, the conservation of entire ecosystems is all the more pressing. The species-by-species approach works well for some animals, particularly those whose numbers have declined in response to overhunting or to some other direct, local, and controllable effect of human activities. For other organisms, a broader approach is required, and the U.S. Fish and Wildlife Service has begun moving in that direction. The service has appointed three regional drainage system recovery teams, one for the Colorado River, one for the eastern Mojave Desert, and a third for the Rio Grande. The latter is responsible for the Clear Creek gambusia, the Leon Springs pupfish, the Pecos bluntnose shiner, the Comanche Springs pupfish, and the Pecos gambusia and has produced a separate recovery plan for each of those endangered fish. The service recently approved the San Marcos Recovery Plan, a new and more comprehensive attempt to protect endangered species. The first recovery plan written for an entire ecosystem, it may represent the wave of future conservation efforts and is therefore worthy of some discussion.

The San Marcos River does not at first glance seem a likely candidate for the attention of federal and state wildlife agencies, conservationists, and nature lovers. Water from a series of limestone springs emerging from the Edwards Aquifer in the city of San Marcos, part way between Austin and San Antonio on Interstate 35, merges to form the San Marcos River. The river seems little more than an oversized creek as it meanders through the town and suburbs, but its clear and voluminous springwaters have nurtured human dwellers for centuries. The Tonkawa Indians named the springs Canycanayesatetio, meaning "warm waters." Comanches later recognized the value of the area and colonized it for themselves. In 1709, a Spanish expedition came upon the springs, and they subsequently became an important rest stop for travelers following the Camino Real, or Royal Road, from Mexico to Nacogdoches. Mexican settlers established San Marcos de Neve about four miles downstream from the springs in 1807 but abandoned it five years later in the face of floods and Indian hostilities.

American settlers began arriving in the San Marcos area in 1835 and used the swift waters for mills, cotton gins, and power plants. For nearly thirty years, until 1895, it was a stop on the famous Chisholm cattle trail. The federal government established an early fish hatchery on the banks of the San Marcos River just below the settlement in the late 1890s. The river was dammed near the headsprings, and the development of the resulting Spring Lake for tourism began in the late twenties with the building of a small, elegant hotel on its shores. Aquarena Springs, Inc., an amusement park company, now owns Spring Lake and offers a variety of rides and shows, including a glass-bottom boat, dancing mermaids, and Ralph, the diving pig. Below the springs today, the river passes through a city park and snakes behind suburban subdivisions and a sewage treatment plant before joining up with the Blanco River 3 miles downstream. From there the San Marcos flows to its confluence with the larger Guadalupe River 35 miles to the southeast.

Despite their unassuming appearance, the first three miles of the San Marcos River constitute a remarkable aquatic ecosystem in respect to the diversity of organisms that exist in its waters. Many of them are found nowhere else in the world. The striking degree of endemism appears to be due primarily to the unusual stability of the springs and stream flow. The San Marcos Springs have never failed, unlike many others, including the larger Comal Springs nearby, which ran dry for six months in 1956. Additionally, the temperature of the San Marcos headwaters remains nearly constant, varying by less than two degrees centigrade annually, and even at the lower end of the spring habitat, temperatures do not vary by much more than five degrees centigrade. That has allowed a number of specialized plants and animals to evolve and prosper in the river's clear, dependable flow.

The unique character of the San Marcos River is matched by its fragility. The city of San Antonio, its suburbs, and several surrounding communities all depend on the same sources of water that feed the San Marcos, and the area has been one of the fastest-growing in the nation. The Bureau of Reclamation predicts that even assuming an unrealistically low growth rate, the demands on the Balcones Fault Zone aquifer will far exceed its recharge capabilities. It is all but certain therefore that the springs at San Marcos will cease flowing at least intermittently within the next twenty to thirty years.

The local urban environment is also undergoing changes. City expansion and suburbanization are altering the drainage pattern so that a much larger amount of surface runoff from storm drains, streets, and other man-made structures now enters the river, affecting temperature, flow, and water quality and leading to increased flooding and erosion. The runoff water also contains various pesticide and herbicide residues, the effects of which are not yet known as far as San Marcos species are concerned. Yet the waters are still alluring enough to attract myriads of swimmers, tubers, and kayakers, whose activities invariably affect organisms dependent on a stable, undisturbed environment. As in other areas, exotic fish species have been introduced either deliberately or inadvertently; some of them prey on native organisms, and others compete with the local species for food and habitat.

Small wonder then that the U.S. Fish and Wildlife Service has officially listed four San Marcos organisms as endangered or threatened. The endangered species are the San Marcos gambusia (*Gambusia georgei*), the fountain darter (*Etheostoma fonticola*), and Texas wild rice (*Zizania texana*); an amphibian, the San Marcos salamander (*Eurycea nana*), is listed as threatened. All four species need an uninterrupted supply of clean, free-flowing, and thermally constant water. Because their numbers are so low and the range of each is so restricted, the service has also designated the entire range of each species as critical habitat in an attempt to preserve the ecosystem as a whole.

The most imperiled of the four species is the San Marcos gambusia, which is believed to survive only within a one-mile stretch of the river from the Interstate 35 bridge to just below Thompson's Island. Even within that range, the population of the small (1½-inch), plainly marked fish is extremely sparse. The San Marcos gambusia was first described as a distinct species only in 1969, and many basic facts about the fish remain to be discovered. It is known that they are highly selective of their habitat, occurring only in quiet, shallow waters of constant temperature, over a muddy substrate with a minimum of aquatic vegetation, but with overhanging trees, bushes, or bridges to afford shade. An increase in aquatic vegetation, the clearing of the river's banks, a disruption of the mud bottom, or a change in temperature could, therefore, have disastrous consequences.

Lack of knowledge about the San Marcos gambusia's food habits and reproduction make it difficult to assess the effects of competition and hybridization with other fish. Two other species of gambusia, the large-spring gambusia (*Gambusia geiseri*) and the mosquito fish, are

San Marcos Salamander

native to the river and much more abundant. Evidence suggests that hybridization between the San Marcos gambusia and the mosquito fish may be a greater threat than previously believed, because of competition from the growing hybrid population. Current efforts to protect the San Marcos gambusia focus on research into its biology and documentation of its past and present status. The Dexter National Fish Hatchery housed a small population, raised from four individuals captured in 1979, but hatchery personnel destroyed the stock after discovering mosquito fish in the culture. The rarity of the San Marcos gambusia makes capture of more individuals for a new propagation attempt extremely difficult. Some people believe that it may already be extinct.

A great deal more is known about the fountain darter (*Etheostoma fonticola*), a reddish brown fish about one inch in length, first described in the 1880s and reported to be abundant in the San Marcos River at that time. It also inhabited the Comal River, a three-mile-long run issuing from Comal Springs in New Braunfels, 25 miles southwest of San Marcos. The fountain darter disappeared from the Comal's waters in the fifties for reasons that are not precisely understood. The fish probably died out when the springs went temporarily dry in 1956, but an earlier treatment of the river's waters with the insecticide rotenone may have contributed to its extirpation.

The fountain darter shares the San Marcos gambusia's need for clean and thermally constant water but prefers vegetated stream bottoms and mats of green algae where it can feast on tiny crustaceans and aquatic larvae. The darter ranges throughout Spring Lake and the upper San Marcos River where suitable habitat is available. Its numbers far exceed those of the San Marcos gambusia, yet that leaves small room for comfort. The darter is similarly susceptible to changes in temperature and modification of the aquatic vegetation on which it depends. Effluent from the sewage treatment plant on the river's banks may have reduced its numbers.

The fountain darter gained some much needed breathing space in 1975 and 1976 when two biologists reintroduced 457 adult darters to Comal Springs, and a reproducing population successfully established itself once again in the Comal River. That second population is extremely vulnerable to the undependable flow of the springs, but its presence, combined with the well-researched population in San Marcos, considerably brightens prospects for the fountain darter's survival.

The San Marcos salamander (*Eurycea nana*) displays many of the same habitat needs and food preferences as the fountain darter, but it is currently restricted to the headwaters of the San Marcos and Comal Rivers. *E. nana* measures less than 2½ inches in length and can alter its predominantly light brown back to a dark brown color in accord with the darkness or lightness of the substrate. In Spring Lake the salamander lurks near the spring outflows and especially in the shallow northern section of the lake in front of the Aquarena Springs Hotel, where dense mats of algae and aquatic moss provide both food and protection from predatory fish, turtles, crayfish, and waterfowl. The abundance of predators makes the moss and algal mats an essential feature of the salamander's habitat, along with clear, free-flowing water at a steady temperature. Many introduced ducks and swans, which populate Spring Lake and amuse visitors to

Aquarena Springs, feed on the aquatic moss and algal mats and thus are prime competitors with the salamander. Their droppings also pollute the moss habitat.

Texas wild rice (*Zizania texana*) has suffered from man's attempts to beautify the San Marcos River. Wild rice is an aquatic grass that grows in large masses rooted to the river's bottom in areas of swiftly flowing water. Left to itself, its flowering heads rise as much as a meter above the surface. William A. Silveus, an attorney and amateur botanist from San Antonio, first recognized the plant as a separate species in 1932. At that time, Texas wild rice grew abundantly in Spring Lake and in the river, as well as in contiguous irrigation ditches. In fact, a local irrigation company had to go to great lengths to keep the dense masses of grass under control. Forty years later, W. Emery, a botanist at Southwest Texas State University in San Marcos, found no Texas wild rice in Spring Lake and only scattered specimens in a 1½-mile segment downstream of the lake. In the lower reaches of the river, there was not a plant to be seen.

Texas wild rice apparently fell victim to a number of human activities. Personnel at Aquarena Springs regularly mowed the aquatic vegetation of Spring Lake to neaten its appearance for visitors. In addition to the plants uprooted in the lake, masses of floating cut vegetation knocked off protruding flowers of wild rice downstream, damaging its reproductive capabilities. Municipal workers likewise periodically raked the river bottom to rid it of vegetation. Exotic plant species were introduced, and they along with native plants were regularly harvested. Raw sewage discharged into the river from the occasionally overloaded treatment facility may also have aided and abetted the destruction of wild rice; runoff water contaminated with pesticides remains a potential threat because of the plant's chemical sensitivity. The effects of a 1980 flood, intensified by the human modification of the river system, wiped out many surviving specimens. Emery's attempts to reintroduce experimental populations eventually failed because introduced nutria ate them and the river's many recreational users disturbed them. Still, his work may represent the best hope for Texas wild rice, as the plant does not appear to be reproducing from seed.

The common threats that those four different water-dependent organisms face underscore the need for ecosystem conservation and for a broad approach to environmental protection that enlists the cooperation of individual landowners, businesses, and municipalities. The city of San Marcos has been active in working to preserve the river, recognizing its fundamental importance not just as a town attraction but as the lifeblood of the community itself. The owners of Aquarena Springs have likewise joined in the effort and are cooperating with the Texas Parks and Wildlife Department's management suggestions concerning the fountain darter, San Marcos salamander, and Texas wild rice. The Nature Conservancy has purchased nine acres along the river that include gambusia habitat and a fragment of wild rice and plans to sell the land to the city of San Marcos. Through the efforts being made for the officially listed species, the entire habitat and its special population of plants and creatures benefit in their struggle to survive.

Opposition understandably arises when obscure and apparently useless animals and plants seem to be receiving preferential treatment at the expense of local citizens and businesses. In 1980, on the same day that the U.S. Fish and Wildlife Service designated critical habitat for the four listed species in the San Marcos system, the Edwards Underground Water District filed suit against the service, fearing that the protection of the four organisms would necessitate costly and impractical remedial actions and provide indirect federal control on pumping from the Edwards Aquifer. The district dropped its suit after being granted a consulting role in the recovery team's efforts. In a separate case, the service withdrew its proposal to list the Devil's River minnow, a denizen of several streams and springs near the Rio Grande in Val Verde County, because of local community opposition. Local landowners argued that conclusive data on the fish's numbers and distribution were lacking and that the case for listing was unconvincing. Again, the community was suspicious of the government's intentions in their area and feared that the presence of an endangered species on their land threatened their own rights as residents and property owners.

Recently the San Antonio City Council has established a controversial program for reducing the city's dependence on the Edwards Aquifer by making better use of the water the city extracts and by building surface reservoirs. The state legislature is also considering a bill to limit pumpage, though rural interests object to restrictions on their rights to draw water from beneath private lands.

The threat of local opposition pales in comparison with the ever-present and overwhelming threat of groundwater depletion and drainage system alteration. Even the most environmentally minded citizens of Texas need and enjoy the benefits that the exploitation of the state's aquifers and rivers has made possible. In a head-on battle between fish and humans, the former would obviously be the first to lose. It's hard to give up something for the sake of a small fish that for the layman is indistinguishable from the common pet-store guppy. How our water life fares, however, is a forward reflection of how Texas and Texans will fare in the near future. If there isn't water enough for a fish the size of a guppy, there surely will not be enough for us.

7 PLANTS

Back to Basics

As is often the case in human affairs, this century's conservation efforts have proceeded in a somewhat haphazard fashion. From big-game management and bird protection, conservation practices gradually evolved to include a broader spectrum of creatures and to take into account the complex links between organisms and their environment. Only within the last twenty years, however, have scientists, lawmakers, conservationists, and bureaucrats engaged in a concerted effort to confront the threats facing the plant kingdom, the foundation of the global ecosystem.

Plants form the basic building block of the food chain because they convert the sun's incoming radiation into organic food, for their own growth and for the sustenance of organisms that feed on them. Complex relationships between plants and local climate, geology, soils, hydrology, topography, and other biota create ecological interdependencies that are often fragile and highly sensitive to change. An estimated 10 percent of the world's approximately 250,000 species of flowering plants could be threatened with extinction by the turn of the coming century. Known uses and as yet undiscovered potentials of various species for medicine, food, and textiles will be lost forever in the swath of extinction. Proven resources will likewise be lost—the wild progenitors of many of today's major food crops are disappearing, and with them their genetic resources, so important for cross-breeding to renew a species' vigor, improve its productivity, and enable it to withstand new pests and diseases.

The specialized feeding and habitat needs of many creatures higher up the food chain compound the seriousness of the plant loss. One botanist has estimated that for every plant species that becomes extinct, an average of ten to thirty other organisms disappear with it. Organisms, both floral and faunal, may also adapt to specific communities of plants with certain characteristics necessary to the dependent organism's survival. Examples of such dependencies in Texas include the needs of the red-cockaded woodpecker and golden-cheeked warbler for particular kinds of trees of a certain density and age. The health and diversity of plant species and communities are thus basic ingredients in the health and diversity of the ecosystem as a whole.

Despite the importance of plants, conservation interest in them lagged far behind efforts for endangered animals. Legislation in the sixties provided protection for vertebrate animals, but it was only with the 1973 Endangered Species Act and the CITES treaty of the same year that plants were afforded limited legal protection. The 1973 Endangered Species Act prevents the federal government from jeopardizing the survival of listed plants but does not prohibit the destruction of threatened or endangered plants on private land. Note how that differs from the protection afforded listed animals, whose harassment or killing is illegal anywhere in the United States.

Why did plant conservation take longer to get under way? Part of the problem was visibility. The critical situation of many rare and endangered plants was all but indiscernible to the untrained eye. Even botanists lacked the resources to undertake a comprehensive inventory of the world's plants. If the protection of birds and mammals seemed a formidable challenge, the protection of plants was overwhelming. Apart from the difficulties posed by the sheer number of plants, public support for plant preservation was not nearly what it was for birds and mammals, which are so much more distinctive in human perceptions. Some observers have even blamed conservationists for the neglect of plants because they tended to equate the health of a particular ecosystem with the stability of a few indicator species, waterfowl in a wetland for example, without taking into account the situation of the whole community.

Classifying the status of species has also presented great challenges to those concerned with plant conservation. Classic rare plants include endemics restricted to a narrow geographical area and often to a specific kind of habitat within that area. The Edwards Plateau and west Texas are major centers of endemism in Texas. Plants found over a wide geographical range but only in certain unusual habitats may also be classified as rare. Some plants may not be restricted to any particular habitat or range but still occur only in low numbers. Sparse populations of a species occurring outside or on the margins of the species' natural range may come under the "rare" category on a state or national list, although they may be common elsewhere.

Many factors may contribute to making a species rare. Some rarities are relicts of former vegetation communities that flourished under past climates and different geologic conditions. Some may be incipients—species just beginning to colonize an area or habitat. Endemics and habitat-specific species have specialized adaptations that sometimes restrict their numbers and spread, but they may also be subject to genetic or environmental barriers. Plants, like animals, may be adapted to certain successional stages of a wider community and so become rare if that stage passes or is disturbed.

Bringing human activities into the picture adds a complicating factor. Human actions may cause a plant to become rare, but more often they instigate or accelerate a decline in an already rare species. Besides habitat modification for buildings, roads, agriculture, and waterworks, human changes include the introduction of new and foreign species, which sometimes crowd out indigenous species; overgrazing by domestic livestock; the accidental introduction of new plant diseases and insect pests; the pollution of water, soil, and air; and the eradication of pollinators (birds, insects, bats) on which particular plants depend for reproduction. In addition, the rarer a plant becomes, the more highly prized it may be by collectors who dig up wild specimens for their gardens. Commercial dealers often capitalize on a plant's rarity; they have been known to wipe out entire populations shortly after the discovery or publication of a rare plant's location.

Many rarities are not in danger of extinction, but others face varying degrees of natural and man-made threats. Conservationists must thus consider an array of philosophical and practical questions concerning which species need protection and the types of threats they face, which populations of rare species should receive highest priority, which aspects of the larger community are most relevant to the rarity's survival and thus how best to manage the habitat as a whole, and how large a population and how many populations are adequate for protection. When plant protection efforts began in earnest during the seventies, the first obstacle to present itself was the nearly total lack of an organized information base from which to start answering those questions. Although scientific plant descriptions have been accumulating in books and journals since the time of Linnaeus, traditional botanical data did not normally include specific details about population numbers, habitat characteristics, and other facts vital to assessing a plant's status and vulnerability to human activities. The 1973 Endangered Species Act therefore directed the Smithsonian Institution to review the situation and make recommendations to the government. Two years later, the Smithsonian issued its report, including a list of more than 3,000 vascular plants in the United States alone that it deemed to be extinct, threatened, or endangered. The U.S. Fish and Wildlife Service subsequently proposed approximately 1,700 plants for federal protection.

The listing procedures proved painfully slow, and by 1978 only 56 of the 1,700 plants had received protection. An amendment to the law imposing a two-year time limit from date of proposal to final listing forced the Fish and Wildlife Service to withdraw from consideration all but the 56 plant taxa that had made it through the maze.

During the same period, the Nature Conservancy, a nonprofit organization dedicated to protecting the nation's biological diversity, began establishing Natural Heritage programs in different states. The programs quickly became highly valued tools in planning for rare plant and animal protection. Each Natural Heritage program was designed to act as an inventory and clearinghouse for specific information on rare or declining species, collating all existing studies and records and conducting field surveys to produce up-to-date knowledge of populations and threats. The programs provide critical aid to national listing efforts and offer solid, site-specific data necessary for land-use planning and long-term species monitoring. Working at the state rather than federal level allows each program to concentrate its efforts and build a manageable data base, to stay in close contact with local researchers, and to target local planning and development needs. The Nature Conservancy, after organizing the initial operations of each program, transfers responsibility to a state agency where ideally the Heritage program becomes part and parcel of state land management.

Thus despite the apparent defeat in listing the 1,700 plant species submitted under the Endangered Species Act, the seventies witnessed the first large-scale coordinated efforts to take stock of rare and threatened plants, precipitating a ground swell of new information and research. Several plants thought to be extinct were rediscovered; others were found to be more numerous or more widely distributed than previously reported. By 1980, the Fish and Wildlife Service had enough information to try again and gave notice that it was considering more than 3,000 plant taxa for possible protection. As of 1988, the service recognized more than 180 plants worldwide as threatened or endangered, most of them in the United States.

The ratio of listed plants to proposed plants unfortunately remains low, and the situation in tropical rain forests, where most of the world's plants grow, is worse still. The task appears yet more daunting when one considers that most conservation efforts are directed at vascular plants: the angiosperms (flowering plants), the gymnosperms (pines and their relatives), and pteridophytes (ferns). Algae, fungi, lichens, mosses, and liverworts have yet to garner much attention. Clearly, it will be impossible to list every species under threat, but the inclusion of plants in conservation laws and programs continues to produce much new information. If properly used, that information will aid in establishing plant preserves and in setting land-use policies less detrimental to rare flora and less harmful to ecosystems as a whole.

Rare Flora of Texas

Diversity of geology, climate, and soils, combined with the state's large size, give Texas the dubious honor of having the third-highest number of rare, threatened, or endangered plant taxa in the nation (Hawaii leads the country with more than a thousand plants; California comes second). Of the state's approximately 5,000 plant taxa, the Texas Natural Heritage Program classifies about 250 as special status (the term "special," which is applied to plant taxa having twenty or fewer discrete populations, is used to avoid the ambiguous designations "rare," "threatened," and "endangered" and to prevent confusion with the legally defined categories "endangered" and "threatened"). The Texas Legislature amended the Parks and Wildlife Code in 1981 to give statutory protection to plants on the federal threatened or endangered lists. Since then, Parks and Wildlife has followed the lead of the U.S. Fish and Wildlife Service and includes on its state list all plants under federal protection. By mid-1988, they numbered 15 endangered and 3 threatened plant species or varieties.

At the center of the state's current efforts for vulnerable flora is the Texas Natural Heritage Program, initiated by the Nature Conservancy in cooperation with the General Land Office in 1983 and now part of the Texas Parks and Wildlife Department. Building on earlier work done by the Rare Plant Study Center at the University of Texas, the Texas Office of Endangered Species, and a number of individual researchers, the Heritage Program is engaged in identifying, mapping, and monitoring the state's rare species. For years, frustrating gaps in knowledge made it difficult to assess whether a species was in fact rare or under threat. One Texas botanist noted that many plant taxa believed to be rare had been inadequately surveyed—because funding for field research was lacking and because the state is so large—and could be more widespread than available studies indicated. Continued monitoring of known rare plants provides a more objective idea of what threats they are facing and of population responses to natural and human-induced changes.

The primary goal of the Heritage Program is to have all that information on hand for state agencies, developers, and other interested parties to consult in planning land-use changes. Whether those groups choose to use the information will, in most cases, be up to them, but it will provide them the opportunity to consider the effect of development on rare species and to weigh alternatives early in the planning process to avoid costly conflicts later. At the least we will no longer be in the pitiful situation of losing species through ignorance of their existence. The research activity also establishes a more knowledgeable basis for determining priorities in plant protection. Since not all vulnerable plants can be protected, and many rare ones are not currently in need of active help, the status assessments contained in the Heritage Program's inventory can direct the limited funding available toward those species that are most endangered.

The following paragraphs examine several Texas plants on the federal and state list of threatened and endangered species. The reader should keep in mind that the Texas Natural Heritage Program considers about 250 plants deserving of special attention, so this discussion is far from exhaustive. In addition, because a comprehensive research program will take several years, the information contained here is necessarily incomplete and subject to change. It does, however, provide a picture of the types of threats that plants face and of the problems encountered by people attempting to preserve the diverse flora of Texas.

Chapter 6 has already introduced what is probably the rarest plant in Texas, *Zizania texana*, or Texas wild rice, one of the San Marcos River's several endemic species. It is typical of other endangered plants in its extremely restricted range but atypical in being aquatic. More prominent on the state's list of endangered or threatened plants are cacti. Seven of the eighteen Texas plants currently receiving state and federal protection belong to the cactus family; their story thus deserves a special look.

Although some cacti, like the familiar Texas prickly pear (*Opuntia lindheimeri*), grow abundantly in many parts of the state and thrive in areas disturbed by human activities, others occur in precariously low numbers. Their habitat and other ecological needs often baffle botanists. Davis' green pitaya (*Echinocereus viridiflorus* var. *davisii*) and Nellie cory cactus (*Coryphantha minima*) represent two different genera of the cactus family, but both grow under similar conditions on low ridges of novaculite in west Texas. Searches have turned up only two populations of the pitaya and three of the cory cactus, despite suitable habitat.

Both cacti are tiny. The Davis' green pitaya is barely an inch tall; its pale yellow flowers bloom in late March and early April and last only two or three days. The Nellie cory cactus grows to an inch and a half in height and is almost spherical in shape. Its rose-purple flowers appear in May, also for a brief two or three days. The pitaya and cory cactus grow in rocky soil and fractured chips of novaculite, often under mats of selaginella, a kind of club moss, and are all but invisible except for the few days when their blooms break through the camouflage. Del Weniger, author of *Cacti of the Southwest*, notes from experience that it requires "a real hands-and-knees effort to search for these diminutive plants in the expanse of the Texas hills."

Unfortunately, such grubbing failed to deter cacti dealers. Soon after A. D. Houghton described Davis' green pitaya in 1931, from a specimen collected by A. R. Davis, himself a commercial dealer, private collectors and dealers rushed to the area and brought out hundreds of plants. The Davis' green pitaya and Nellie cory cactus remain prized trophies for rare-cacti lovers, and dealers all over the world know their precise locations. Another surge of collection took place in the sixties, but more recently the green pitaya population, at least, appears to be holding its own.

Why the two cacti grow where they do and not in similar areas nearby is not yet understood but may be the result of dispersal difficulties. Some as yet undiscovered soil requirement may also play a role. Reproduction in both species still needs a great deal of research. The recovery plans, completed in 1984, urge funding for further examination of all those questions, but an equally important priority is to determine the effect and extent of human collecting. Although natural events and habitat modification through brush clearing, road building, grazing, and other activities have all taken their toll, it is the enthusiastic attachment that humans feel for the tough, thorny cacti that may ultimately cause the demise of certain species. While the various ecological factors in plant extinctions remain obscure, overcollecting represents a clear threat to species with limited numbers and range and has been especially devastating for cacti.

The cacti's problems are compounded by their easy collection and marketability. Unlike many plants, some cacti may be dug up and transplanted into pots with little difficulty. Thousands can be collected cheaply, and even if many rot unsold, dealers can still turn a profit. In west Texas, a prime area for cactus rustlers, itinerant workers earn a few cents per plant and scour the landscape to gain their daily sustenance. Roadside stores and gas stations sell cacti to passing motorists and send thousands more off to wholesalers elsewhere. H. A. Harrison, a Methodist minister and cactus enthusiast from Louisiana, reported on the pathetic scenes he observed during one trip to west Texas. In town after town he found small-time dealers with piles of dry and rotting cacti of every local species. A motel manager said he sold "the damn things to make a buck"; behind his motel, thousands of cacti, riddled with rot, baked in the sun. Serious dealers show no such laxity and quickly ship truckloads of cacti off to lucrative urban markets. When Harrison inquired about the destination of one particular batch, a driver warned him in a burst of temper and vile language not to ask questions about things that didn't concern him. "The sheer volume of plants being removed," Harrison wrote, "seemed to me to constitute a fundamental violation of creation."

In the past, botanists' descriptions and publications about new cactus species have almost invariably released a deluge of dealers on the newly discovered plant's range. The rarest cacti sell for hundreds of dollars, and endangered species are naturally among the most highly prized. One lovely scarlet-flowered species, Lloyd's hedgehog cactus (*Echinocereus lloydii*), had the good fortune to remain hidden for years even though Nathaniel Lord Britton and J. N. Rose had included it in their four-volume classic, *The Cactaceae*, in the twenties. "Tuna Springs, Texas," was the only information the two authors could obtain regarding the plant's location, and since Tuna Springs rarely appeared on any road map, dealers remained frustrated in their attempts to find the cactus. Thus it grew undisturbed and, according to Del Weniger, "rather commonly within its small range." Only in the sixties did the news get out that Tuna Springs had been a stop on the old stagecoach route out of Fort Stockton in Pecos County. Collectors and dealers quickly descended on the area and began pulling up specimens. Highway construction exacerbated the damage, and in 1979 Lloyd's hedgehog cactus joined the list of endangered plants, its era of quietude ended. Recently, additional populations have been found in Brewster County and in Hudspeth and Culberson counties extending into southern New Mexico. Whether the news of those discoveries will be to the detriment or advantage of *E. lloydii* only time and careful monitoring will tell.

In fairness to responsible cactus enthusiasts, they, like falconers, have the potential to be valuable assets in conservation. The Conservation Committee of the Cactus and Succulent Society of America has urged the society's members to make their skills and knowledge available to state and federal agencies. Conservation need not interfere with the cactus hobby. Many cacti can be grown from seeds or cuttings; indeed, the high prices of newly discovered species eventually fall as they come into seed and vegetative propagation. Some cacti prove difficult to propagate; the Conservation Committee has suggested that the society fund research on those species and on methods for their propagation as a positive contribution to cactus protection. In the meantime, two sets of people must shoulder a large burden. As with all species, the cooperation of owners of land on which rare cacti occur is absolutely essential. In the sixties, a rancher allowed collectors on his land, and they dug up his entire population of Nellie cory cactus. The second responsibility lies with buyers of cacti not to purchase rare plants collected from the wild in cases where their survival is jeopardized. As such a distinction is impossible to make without some sort of verification system, buyers should be informed about rare cacti and wary of dealers whom they do not know or trust.

Although the cacti family has the most representatives on the list of endangered and threatened plants in Texas, many species from other families are similarly at risk. The Garden Clubs of America have lauded the Texas poppy mallow (*Callirhoe scabriuscula*) as one of the state's most beautiful wildflowers. The *Callirhoe* genus includes the widespread and colorful wine-cups, spring-flowering herbs that have colonized many of the state's fields and roadsides. *C. scabriuscula*, by contrast, was thought to occur only on a small area of windblown sand in Runnels County, in west-central Texas, and was among the rarest members of its genus. Sutton Hays, an Army surgeon with the El Paso and Fort Yuma Wagon Road Expedition, first collected specimens of the two- to four-foot-high perennial in the latter half of the nineteenth century near the Colorado River in Texas. Benjamin Robinson came across Hays's specimens in Harvard University's Gray Herbarium and named it *Callirhoe scabriuscula* in 1897.

The Texas poppy mallow grows exclusively in deep loose sand carried by the Colorado River and deposited by wind on top of the river's floodplain. The result is a somewhat localized soil type highly susceptible to erosion. *C. scabriuscula* may be a relict species, and botanists are examining its reproduction strategy as one key to its apparent rareness. Agricultural clearing, livestock grazing, and highway construction have all reduced habitat for the Texas poppy mallow, but the greatest threat may come from commercial sand mining. A 1979 survey located sixteen populations of the species, ranging in size from a few square meters to about 1,600 square meters, but by 1983 sand extraction had wiped out the largest, and the others showed a marked decline.

The Texas poppy mallow joined the federal list of endangered species in early 1981, and a recovery team completed its report four years later. Besides pointing out the need for landowner cooperation and further studies of C. *scabriuscula*'s biology, the team called for surveys of windblown sand deposits along the upper reaches of the Colorado and other rivers to the north. In 1987, field researchers located five additional populations of the species. Further searches in 1988 failed to locate any new populations.

The story of Navasota ladies' tresses (*Spiranthes parksii*) illustrates well the problems and pitfalls in plant conservation. The *Spiranthes* genus belongs to the orchid family and includes more than 300 species. The spiral spike of flowers resembling a braid of hair topping off a long slender stalk marks orchids of this genus and gives the plant its common name. In 1945, H. B. Parks found a population of ladies' tresses near the Navasota River in east-central Texas. The botanist believed that they belonged to one of the *Spiranthes* species already known in the state, but two years later, Donovan Correll declared Parks's specimens to be representatives of a new species, which Correll named *Spiranthes parksii.*

The newly named ladies' tresses were not seen again for more than thirty years, despite sporadic searches in the forties, fifties, and seventies. Some botanists believed that the species had passed into extinction, and the Smithsonian report listed it as such. Others thought that Parks's specimens were simply abnormal representatives of some other *Spiranthes* species.

In October of 1978, two University of Toronto botanists came across *Spiranthes* specimens on the bank of a temporary stream in oak woodlands north of Navasota. Some of the plants among the grasses clearly belonged to *Spiranthes cernua,* one of the more widely distributed species of ladies' tresses, but others bore all the marks of *Spiranthes parksii.* A few hundred yards away, the two botanists discovered thirteen more of the elusive orchids on the bank of yet another temporary stream. In all twenty specimens of S. *parksii* turned up that day.

The U.S. Fish and Wildlife Service gave official protection to S.

Navasota Ladies' Tresses

parksii as an endangered species in May 1982. At the time, only the few plants found in 1978 were known, but further surveys by Hugh Wilson of Texas A&M University later that year turned up a hundred or more at four sites in Brazos County. Despite the new discoveries, the survival of S. *parksii* was still at risk. The expansion of Texas A&M and the growth of the College Station–Bryan area in general represented the most immediate threat. As called for in the Endangered Species Act, any project or activity requiring federal participation or approval must take into account the potential impact on endangered or threatened species. In July of 1983, the first conflict over the ladies' tresses arose when the Fish and Wildlife Service issued a jeopardy opinion to the federal Highway Administration, stating that the proposed expansion of State Highway 6 near Bryan would likely damage S. *parksii*'s chances of survival.

Following that opinion, U.S. Fish and Wildlife contracted with Wilson to conduct a new survey with the help of the Texas Highway Department. The survey team discovered several new populations tallying 1,816 individuals scattered across four Texas counties. Assuming the survey missed a substantial number of plants, the recovery team later estimated the total population at more than 5,000. The Fish and Wildlife Service subsequently reevaluated its earlier opinion, and in September of 1983 issued a new opinion stating that it no longer believed that the highway expansion would endanger S. *parksii*'s continued existence.

Spiranthes parksii still faces several threats. Most populations occur on private land, so effective protection is hard to obtain. In addition, the largest population lies astride a massive seam of lignite, and mining would certainly destroy much of the prime habitat. The expansion of light industry, if not well planned, could also prove destructive. If the two primary population centers of S. *parksii*, which are the most threatened by industrial expansion, are wiped out, an estimated 20 percent of present numbers would still remain, but the margin of survival would be greatly reduced.

Protection efforts are proceeding for S. *parksii*, mainly on land belonging to the Texas Municipal Power Authority, which under state and federal law must help to mitigate any adverse effect it has on the plant. Both conservationists and the power authority have run into difficulties in this initial encounter between development and an endangered plant. The power authority is cooperating, but because information concerning *S. parksii* is still incomplete and because it is the first major case of its kind in Texas, guidelines and criteria as to exactly what constitutes adequate protection remain uncertain, making joint efforts difficult for all involved. For its part, the power authority is willing to set aside a protected area for the ladies' tresses, but state conservationists have yet to find an authority to fund and oversee its management.

Proper management of any area eventually set aside will depend on understanding more about *S. parksii*'s biology and its place in the surrounding ecosystem. The ecological factors that produce the open oak woods it inhabits are complex; if the area receives complete protection some of those factors may no longer come into play and the forces of natural succession might produce a heavily wooded habitat, unsuitable for the very plant that the protection was initiated to benefit. Thus protection, research, and careful management must all go hand in hand if conservation is to progress with any effectiveness.

Preserving Communities

Anyone who has traveled through Texas knows that the state is a vast patchwork of different landscapes, ranging from the well-watered woodlands of the east to the dry expanse of high plains in the west, and from rich productive soils of the Blackland Prairie in the northern and central part of the state to subtropical shrublands in its most southern extension. Although those landscapes still impress native and visitor alike, immense changes have taken place that have tended to homogenize the state's natural diversity.

This book has examined the impact of that transformation on certain plant and animal species. The species-by-species approach to conservation aims at preserving the genetic diversity of the state's flora and fauna. There are many biological communities across the state, however, that may not contain individual endangered species but that are nonetheless threatened as a whole. A biological community can be defined as an interacting system of organisms linked by the effects they have on one another and by their shared relationship to the surrounding environment, in much the same way that a human community works. Just as many traditional human communities are fast disappearing, so too are many plant and animal communities that were familiar to native Americans and later to pioneers who came to Texas in the nineteenth century. The famous Pineywoods of southeast Texas have mostly fallen to timber production, and though pine forests remain, they are in fact pine plantations, cultivated for timber or pulp wood. Species and age diversity of trees have been lost, and human forces now maintain the simplified ecosystem. Communities of bottomland hardwoods that once grew in dense thickets along the bayous, streams, and rivers of the east and southeast, and into southcentral Texas, are likewise disappearing. In addition to the impact of logging on the woodlands, modifications of natural flooding regimes have reduced their extent and diversity.

It is the prairies, however, that are the most deeply embedded in Texas culture and history. Vast grasslands once extended from Texas through the Middle West and into southern Canada. The newly arrived Europeans had never seen anything like that ocean of grass. The English had no word for it and so followed the lead of French explorers, calling the immense grasslands "prairies," a term of French origin meaning "meadow." New settlers were quick to recognize the fertility of the soil that lay beneath the prairie grasses and the grasses' potential as a seemingly boundless pasture for livestock. Indians and animals on which they subsisted were killed or driven from the land; row crops replaced native grasses, and cattle grazed where bison once roamed.

Texas was America's largest prairie state, and early settlers eagerly headed for its native grasslands, passing up the woodlands of the east and difficult conditions on the coastal plain. The most fertile land lay in the Blacklands – 12 million acres of tallgrass prairies with scattered trees stretching from the Red River across east-central Texas to San Antonio. Today less than 5,000 acres of the region's native grasslands remain, mostly in small patches of a few acres scattered over their former range. Although grasslands may look monotonous to the human eye, they support a surprisingly diverse flora and fauna, much of it hidden in the grasses and within the soil. Larger prairie dwellers are now gone – bison, wolves, pronghorns, and elk – as are the Indians, who may have extended the borders of grasslands by setting them alight in the pursuit of game.

Ecologists at the Natural Heritage Program are studying and mapping the rare biological communities of Texas to provide the groundwork needed to maintain representative examples of healthy natural systems. Unlike endangered species, endangered communities receive no protection unless the owners of the land—be they public agencies, private individuals, companies, or organizations—provide it themselves. The Heritage Program has created a list of priority communities in need of protection and keeps interested parties informed as to where action is needed. In 1986, the Nature Conservancy purchased 114 acres of Clymer's Meadow, a 540-acre tract of Blackland prairie in Hunt County in north Texas. The tract is the largest surviving section of the original Blacklands and topped the Heritage Program's priority list.

The U.S. Fish and Wildlife Service and Texas Parks and Wildlife also take an interest in community protection, and together with organizations like the Nature Conservancy, they can preserve small sections of native habitat. As always, however, effective protection requires that the human inhabitants of the land take the time and interest to understand the natural systems and to work in tandem with them. In the case of Clymer's Meadow, for example, cooperation between its owner and the Nature Conservancy proved successful. Knowing it was a special piece of land, the owner of the Clymer's Meadow tract contacted the Nature Conservancy when he decided to sell and gave back to Texas a valuable part of its heritage.

Plant conservation has made large strides since its late start in the seventies, and nonbotanists in government agencies and environmental organizations now have a great deal more information to aid them in their planning decisions. According to the International Union for the Conservation of Nature, as of 1970 only Belgium had produced a list of its threatened flora, and only one man, Ronald Melville, was working to assess the global situation of endangered plants. By 1986, all but twelve of the world's developed countries had produced national lists of endangered flora, and on a global scale, more than 15,000 plants had been cataloged as rare, threatened, or endangered. Much remains to be done. In the past, most research has addressed temperate regions and islands, although about two thirds of the world's plant taxa occur in tropical areas. Progress proceeds slowly in tropical regions, where obscure, sometimes unknown species continue to fall victim to rain-forest clearing.

The struggle to understand more thoroughly the world of plants has challenged the conservation process as never before. As we explore the lesser known plants and animals, and the communities of which they form a part, complexities and ambiguities in nature's dynamics become far more apparent than when we focus on, for example, the protection of a large and familiar mammal. The clear and simple concept of preservation appears more complicated when one carefully dissects natural processes and human modifications and their varying effects.

Yet the importance of considered and thoughtful conservation shines all the more brightly now that the plant kingdom, the foundation of all life, is finally receiving the attention due it. Conservation in that sense means gearing our lives and works toward greater knowledge of the world we inhabit, and with that knowledge, using our resources more wisely and our dominating power more gently. In the intricacies of plant life we recognize the complex web of relations in which we, too, have a place.

8 WILDLIFE IN AN URBAN AGE

In excess of 80 percent of Texans live in urban places. The 1980 census placed 3.1 million people in Dallas–Fort Worth, 3.5 million in Houston, and 1.1 million in San Antonio, the state's three major metropolitan areas. One in three residents make their homes in one of those urban centers, which continue to engulf prairies and woodlands—the aboriginal living spaces for native wildlife—to accommodate the steady influx of new Texans.

Habitat change typified by the pattern of suburban development also includes the expansion of cropland, brush control and pasture improvement, river impoundments, and woodland clearing. Such humanly induced transformations of the face of Texas date back to impresario schemes in the 1820s. Today, every region reflects human activities in varying degrees. Crops grow on about 20 million acres. About 6.75 million acres support irrigation agriculture, mostly on the High Plains, replacing the shortgrasses, mesquite, shinnery oak, and sagebrush that once characterized that region. Five million acres in wheat, 4.8 million acres in cotton, and 3.95 million acres in grain sorghum head up an impressive list of cash crops. Add to those statistics 15 million head of cattle, 2 million sheep, 1.5 million goats, and sizable numbers of hogs and horses, and one recognizes the proud image of Texas as an agricultural emporium. The state places third in the nation in regard to cash receipts from farm and ranch products.

But there is more behind those impressive economic figures. They demonstrate how much the face of Texas has been changed to give such returns. The Blackland Prairie, that wedge of dark soils arcing from San Antonio northward to east of Dallas and through to the Red River, is dramatically altered. The plow has bitten deeply to grow bountiful crops of corn and cotton for well over a century, and today the arable region is densely settled, with Austin, Temple, and Waco inserted between its southern and northern margins. Native bison, prairie chickens, antelope, and wolves have long since gone, as have most of the deer, turkeys, quail, and aboriginal vegetation.

The blackland is on the western perimeter of the key Rolling Prairies zone that the Father of Texas, Stephen F. Austin, and subsequent pioneers identified as best for settlement. The warm, well-watered, fertile, undulating zone lay between the humid lowland plagued by fever and insects along the coast and the elevated west, or mountain, zone of Texas, whose deserts and plains were the home for Indians and herds of migratory buffalo. The Rolling Prairies offered great promise for settlement. They provided timber for construction, possessed numerous openings and prairies for stock, had excellent soils for planting, and allowed access to navigable waterways. Colonists cleared the region, turning the wilderness into a veritable man-made garden. Promoters spread that image to attract immigrants who would refashion the landscape to resemble civilized places in the East. They excluded those organisms that impeded their operations or threatened their livelihoods. They tended other organisms that were materially useful or decorative.

After the 1900s, a burgeoning petrochemical industry complemented that foundation of agriculture. Industry altered the environment still more, contributing to water pollution, wirescapes, and modern highways. The face of Texas shows such novel features that in many places bear no resemblance to earlier ones.

Some animals have adjusted to modern landscapes better than others. Adaptable species like raccoons, rodents, insect-eating birds (titmice, wrens, chickadees), as well as granivorous ones (cowbirds, blackbirds, grackles), prosper in croplands and around growing towns and cities. They proliferate (along with certain alien organisms) while more specialized species, intolerant of human activities, falter and disappear. In other words, creatures capable of pioneering new or disturbed environments benefit from agriculture and industry; those that don't succeed in new situations we label as failures in need of our intervention and support to survive.

We tend also to regard the less adaptable species as unnatural, existing only in special refuges. That approach reflects a fundamental sense of being outside nature's system, always ready to improve upon it as we fashion new ecosystems or prop up sets of new linkages between species by introducing new organisms or eliminating existing ones. All life-forms except our own must adjust to those conditions, for we regard ourselves as beyond any of the bounds that connect us with the aboriginal environment. Rather than adjust, for example, to the natural hydrology of Texas, we have rearranged river flows by building huge reservoirs and tapping into artesian water supplies in our quest to make west Texas, the so-called Great American Desert, bloom.

Rather than recognize or impose constraints, we have developed a Promethean complex that feeds upon our self-image. Texans have formulated ever grander expectations and amusements. In the process, they have promoted bigger and better new animals, including a cadre of foreign, mainly game mammals, which are prospering in their variety and abundance.

Back in the thirties the introduction of nilgai antelope, an Indian ungulate, to the King Ranch sparked what became a trend among ranchers, who imported and released a veritable Noah's ark of wildlife. Over the past half-century the number of foreign species and their populations have increased dramatically. The first statewide survey in 1963 turned up 13 mammal species and 13,000 animals. A recent Parks and Wildlife survey (1984) counted 59 species represented by a minimum of 120,000 individuals. Axis deer and blackbuck antelope are most numerous. The fourfold increase in variety and almost tenfold increase in abundance make Texas unique—nowhere else in North America is there more exotic game in greater numbers. Though that situation may prove lucrative to ranchers, it may not be as attractive to them in the long term. Studies have shown that several key exotics may cope with drought more successfully than native whitetails and even outcompete them.

This book speaks to the issue of divorcing ourselves from the land and from the mechanisms that support a varied flora and fauna. One reason we feel so separated from the rhythms and cycles of the seasons and years is that we have so quickened the pace of our own lives as to lose contact with the fundamental issues of birth and death. Most of us spend our lives in sequestered places, oblivious to the vagaries of feast and famine, drought and flood, tempest and tranquillity, for we do not need to know how the land maintains itself or how living things group together in associations or communities to insure their survival over the long term by adjusting to environmental change. In other words, urban life and its material conveniences buffer us from having to deal with or learn about ways of producing foods, fibers, and liquids. Others do that for us by acting as intermediaries between the fields, pastures, or orchards and the retail stores where we purchase our packaged produce. We have reduced our linkages with the environment to functional, efficient facts, and we have disparaged any sense of historical interplay by insisting that new gadgets, be they biocides, machines, or guns, make the old simply archaic and redundant. The experiences of earlier generations in settling Texas are so different from our own that while we can admire them for sentimental reasons, we cannot embrace them as part of our ordinary relations with nature.

In the 150 years since Texans declared their independence from Mexico, they have toiled to establish a level of self-sufficiency and a mastery of the land that would make their future secure. Our current stage of development, notes writer Larry McMurtry, involves the greater expression of imagination and human creativity to fully satisfy human aspirations and needs. That position includes a sense of connection with the environment and involvement with the land as a repository of meaning. All of us have needs that bind us to the earth, beyond the requirement for material sustenance. One of them is the affective bond that makes us feel at home. It is a desire to dwell or to make a house into a home. We impress our own personality on the places in which we live by the routines we set up and by the various objects, colors, and ways of arranging and combining them.

Texans have expressed "at homeness" through a strong sense of regional identity that is historically grounded in initial nationhood and political independence. They have been less articulate, however, in expressing that connection with the physiographic and biological character of the state, except to pit themselves against nature, resulting in the exploitation of resources. The idea that the environment and the wildlife that give it character and distinction are part and parcel of our own communal health and well-being, at least according to social and intellectual historians, has tended to be submerged by the quest for material self-sufficiency. So where do these failures in vision lead us?

The answer rests within ourselves. Not surprisingly, the urban age has generated a sense of or perhaps a need for communion with the very environment we have been drawing ourselves away from all these years. In our reaction against impersonal, alien urban forms and structures, we search for knowledge and understanding of vital, living environments. This book has demonstrated that although the threats to wild animals and plants are massive, we have initiated the means by which we might protect and conserve those fellow beings. Simple ignorance will no longer lead to biological destruction. We cannot, however, leave that vast amount of new information to professional scientists and wildlife managers and expect them to bear the responsibility for curing our ecological ills. "Ecology" derives from the Greek word "oikos," referring originally to the household and its maintenance. The earth is our only home; we have in our hands and our heads better means to maintain it than ever before. To use them requires patience and small, steady steps beginning at our front door. Texas occupies only one small part of our planet, but within it revolve worlds of life.

SOURCES

There are basic sources of information about the distribution and numbers of wild animals and plants in Texas. Two books by David J. Schmidly, *Mammals of Trans-Pecos Texas* (1977) and *Texas Mammals East of the Balcones Fault Zone* (1983), give background details for mammals. William B. Davis, *The Mammals of Texas* (Bulletin No. 41, Texas Parks and Wildlife Department, revised 1974) is useful although somewhat dated. Harry C. Oberholser, *The Bird Life of Texas* (two volumes, 1974) lists bird species, distribution, and numbers throughout the state. General information on progress and problems in rare plant research can be found in Hugh Synge's edited volume, *The Biological Aspects of Rare Plant Conservation* (1981), and in *Rare Plant Conservation: Geographical Data Organization* (1981), edited by Larry E. Morse and Mary Sue Henifin.

The Endangered Species Technical Bulletin published by the U.S. Fish and Wildlife Service, reprinted by the School of Natural Resources, University of Michigan, Ann Arbor, provides updated and detailed information about the nation's threatened and endangered organisms. It is a vital source for issues or problems related to animal and plant conservation. *Restoring America's Wildlife* (U.S. Fish and Wildlife Service, Washington, D.C., 1987) covers primarily game mammal and bird restoration and management. Various authors deal with such game animals as the pronghorn antelope, bighorn sheep, and wild turkey, and nongame wildlife conservation on a state-by-state basis. *Vanishing Fishes of North America* (1983), by R. Dana Ono, James D. Williams, and Anne Wagner, is very useful.

This book has drawn from all of those sources. Additionally we have referred to different U.S. Fish and Wildlife recovery plans such as the *San Marcos River Recovery Plan* (1984) and others that pertain to individual organisms. The U.S. Fish and Wildlife Service, Biological Service Program, has summarized information on a number of endangered birds, including the American peregrine falcon, whooping crane, and bald eagle. The service has compiled *Endangered Species of Texas and Oklahoma* (1984), which lists the animals and plants most in need of conservation.

On a state basis, *Texas Parks and Wildlife* magazine, *Texas Parks and Wildlife News*, and project reports associated with the federal Aid in Wildlife Restoration Act are all excellent sources of up-to-date information. The *Nature Conservancy News* and the Texas Nature Conservancy magazine, *Horizons*, supply a perspective from the private sector of conservation. Additionally, local chapters of the National Audubon Society, the Sierra Club, and sportsmens groups can comment on specific issues.

Biologists and other experts involved in research with endangered species may be contacted through the Texas Parks and Wildlife Department Endangered Species Program and the Texas Heritage Program.

Further Reading

Adams, Andy. *Cattle Brands.* Boston: Houghton, Mifflin. 1934.

Bailey, Vernon. *Biological Survey of Texas.* North American Fauna 25. Washington, D.C.: Government Printing Office. 1905.

Bean, Michael J. "The Endangered Species Program." In *National Audubon Wildlife Report 1986.* Edited by Roger L. Di Silvestro. New York: National Audubon Society 1986

Bedichek, Roy. *Adventures with a Texas Naturalist.* Austin: University of Texas Press. 1961.

Bigony, Mary-Love. "Back Home on the Range." *Texas Parks and Wildlife* October 1982:2–7.

Blair, W. Frank. "The Biotic Provinces in Texas." *Texas Journal of Science* 2 (1950):93–117.

Blankinship, David R., and Kirke A. King. "A Probable Sighting of 23 Eskimo Curlews in Texas." *American Birds* 38 (Nov.–Dec. 1984):1066–1067.

Burr, J. G. "A Texas Grizzly Hunt." *Texas Game and Fish* 6 (August 1948):4–5.

Campbell, Faith. "The Appropriations History of the 1973 Endangered Species Act." *Endangered Species Update* 5 (August 1988):20–25.

Carley, Curtis J. *Status Summary: The Red Wolf* Canis rufus. Endangered Species Report 7. Albuquerque: U.S. Fish and Wildlife Service. 1979.

Carson, Burch. "Man, the Greatest Enemy of Desert Bighorn Mountain Sheep." *Texas Game, Fish and Oyster Commission Bulletin* 21 (1941):1–23.

Craig, Gerald. "The Peregrine Falcon." *Audubon Wildlife Report 1986.* Edited by Robert L. Di Silvestro. New York: National Audubon Society. 1986.

Doughty, Robin W. *Wildlife and Man in Texas: Environmental Change and Conservation.* College Station: Texas A&M University Press. 1983.

——. "Sea Turtles in Texas: A Forgotten Commerce." *Southwestern Historical Quarterly* 88 (July 1984):43–70.

Ehrlich, Paul, and Anne Ehrlich. *Extinction.* New York: Random House. 1981.

Fleming, Kay M. ". . . To Trade for Turkeys." *Texas Parks and Wildlife* June 1981:22–25.

Gard, Wayne. "The Moar Brothers, Buffalo Hunters." *Southwestern Historical Quarterly* 63 (July 1959):31–45.

Gehlbach, Frederick R. *Mountain Islands and Desert Seas.* College Station: Texas A&M University Press. 1981.

Haley, J. Evetts. *The XIT Ranch of Texas.* Norman: University of Oklahoma Press. 1953.

Harrington, H. A. "The Need for Protection of Our Native Cacti." *Cactus and Succulent Journal* 52 (1980):224–226.

Hollon, W. Eugene, and Ruth L. Butler. *William Bollaert's Texas.* Norman: University of Oklahoma Press. 1956.

Jobman, Wallace G., and Maurice E. Anderson. "Potential Present Range of the Black-Footed Ferret as of January 1, 1981." U.S. Fish and Wildlife Service, P.O. Box 250, Pierre, SD 57501.

Johnson, James E., and John N. Rinne. "The Endangered Species Act and Southwest Fishes." *Fisheries* 7 (July–Aug. 1982):2–8.

Jones, Monty. "Group Links U.S. Timber Cuts to Decline of Rare Woodpecker." *Austin American-Statesman*, Sept. 6, 1987

Jurries, Royce W. *Attwater Prairie Chicken.* Austin: Texas Parks and Wildlife Dept. 1979.

Krausse, Henry. "San Marcos River a War Zone in Fight Against Extinction." *Austin American-Statesman*, April 9, 1989.

Leggett, Mike. "Project: Bighorn." *Austin American-Statesman*, Nov. 13, 1988.

—. "The Eagles Have Landed." *Austin American-Statesman*, Jan. 17, 1989.

Leopold, Aldo. *A Sand County Almanac.* New York: Oxford University Press. 1966.

Loughmiller, Campbell, and Lynn Loughmiller, eds. *Big Thicket Legacy.* Austin: University of Texas Press. 1977.

Lyons, Gary. "At Long Last: Protection for Endangered Cacti." *Cactus and Succulent Journal* 52 (1980):229, 232.

Marcy, Randolph B. *Exploration of the Red River of Louisiana, in the year 1852.* Washington, D.C.: A.O.P. Nicholson. 1854.

Oldfield, Margery. *The Value of Conserving Genetic Resources.* Washington, D.C.: National Park Service. 1984.

Pulich, Warren M. *The Golden-cheeked Warbler.* Austin: Texas Parks and Wildlife Dept. 1976.

Ramsey, Charles W. *Texotics.* Texas Parks and Wildlife Bulletin 49. Austin: Texas Parks and Wildlife Dept. 1968.

Simmons, George F. *Birds of the Austin Region.* Austin: University of Texas Press. 1925.

Synge, Hugh. "Plants in Danger: What Do We Know?" *IUCN Bulletin* 17 (Jan.–March 1986).

Tewes, Mike E., and Daniel D. Everett. "Status and Distribution of the Endangered Ocelot and Jaguarundi in Texas." In *Cats of the World: Biology, Conservation and Management.* Edited by S. D. Miller and D. D. Everett. 1982.

Thompson, Bruce C., Floyd E. Potter, and William C. Brownlee. *Management Plan for the American Alligator in Texas.* Austin: Texas Parks and Wildlife Dept. 1984.

U.S. Fish and Wildlife Service. *Clear Creek Gambusia* (Gambusia heterochir) *Recovery Plan.* Albuquerque, 1980.

—. *Comanche Springs Pupfish* (Cyprinodon elegans) *Recovery Plan.* Albuquerque, 1980.

—. *Endangered and Threatened Wildlife and Plants,* Jan. 1, 1986. Washington, D.C., 1986.

—. *Houston Toad Recovery Plan.* Albuquerque, 1984.

—. *San Marcos River Recovery Plan.* Albuquerque, 1984.

—. *Whooping Crane Recovery Plan.* Albuquerque, 1986.

Wilson, D. E. "Adaptability of Louisiana Wild-Trapped Eastern Turkey in Pine-Hardwood Release Sites in East Texas." Federal Aid Project No. W-108-R. Texas Parks and Wildlife, Austin. 1985.

Woody, Jack B. "Kemp's Ridley Sea Turtle." In *Audubon Wildlife Report 1986*. Edited by Robert L. Di Silvestro. New York: National Audubon Society. 1986.

Associations and Programs for Endangered Species

Center for Environmental Education
1201 W. 24th Street
Austin, TX 78703

Especially good for marine animals.

Texas Organization for Endangered Species
P.O. Box 12773
Austin, TX 78711-2773

An association of people professionally and personally interested in wildlife, who are compiling lists of species in trouble and promoting conservation plans and strategies for various animals and plants.

Texas Parks and Wildlife Department
Texas Heritage Program and
Nongame and Endangered Species Program
4200 Smith School Road
Austin, TX 78744

Both programs track threatened and endangered native plants and animals and have official links with endangered species specialists in the U.S. Fish and Wildlife Service, both in its regional office (for Texas, Oklahoma, and New Mexico) at P.O. Box 1306, Albuquerque, New Mexico 87103 (phone 505-766-2321), and in its Division of Endangered Species, Washington, D.C. 20240 (phone 703-235-2771).

Appendix 1
Wildlife Conservation in Texas

1861 First game law establishes a closed season for quail on Galveston Island

1874 First fish law prohibits seining in certain coastal waters

1879 A fish law requires fish ladders for dams and establishes the Office of Fish Commissioner. Joe H. Dinkins appointed (1879–1880)

1883 A total of 130 counties claim exemptions from all game laws

1885 Fish Commission is abolished

1895 Office of Fish and Oyster Commissioner is established. I. P. Kibbe appointed (1895–1906)

1899 State Audubon Society is founded

1903 Five-year closed season is set for pronghorn antelope, bighorn sheep, pheasants; the sale of those animals, plus deer and nongame birds, is prohibited

1907 Game Department is added to Office of Fish and Oyster Commissioner. R. H. Wood, commissioner

1909 Hunting licenses are required, except for residents in home and adjacent counties

1916 Migratory Treaty Act between U.S. and Canada sets limits and closed seasons on migratory birds such as waterfowl and doves

1919 Five-year closed season is placed on wood ducks, and protection is given for turkey hens

1923 Forty-five wardens are employed from the game fund

1929 Six individuals are appointed to Texas Fish and Game Commission. First executive secretary, W. M. Tucker

1935	Texas Wildlife Research Unit is established in cooperation with Texas A&M University (discontinued in 1954)
1937	Federal Pittman-Robertson Act requires an excise tax on sporting arms and ammunition for reapportionment to states (Texas has consistently ranked high in funding for wildlife.)
1942	First issue of *Texas Game and Fish* (became *Texas Parks and Wildlife*, 1965)
1944	First open season on pronghorn antelope (since 1903)
1950	Federal Dingell-Johnson Act requires excise tax on sport fishing equipment for reapportionment to states
1953	First antlerless deer season in Texas (for does in Mason, Gillespie, and Kerr counties)
1960	About half of Texas counties come under the regulatory authority of the Game and Fish Commission
1963	Texas Parks and Wildlife is established through merger of state Parks Board with Game and Fish Commission
1964	Open season on aoudad, or barbary sheep, in Palo Duro Canyon (stocked there in 1958)
1966	First comprehensive plan for outdoor recreation in Texas
1970	Point system is set up for waterfowl hunting, and studies are initiated for rare and endangered animals
1973	Texas Endangered Species Act charges Texas Parks and Wildlife to investigate nongame and endangered species
1974	First state list of endangered species is published, listing five mammals, nine birds, two reptiles, five amphibians, and five fishes
1975	First eastern and hybrid turkeys are released in Texas

1977 State list expands to include 46 endangered species and 81 protected nongame species (the equivalent of the U.S. Fish and Wildlife Service's "threatened" category)

1979 First introduction of pronghorn antelope from another state —100 pronghorns from Wyoming are released on three North Texas ranches

1981 Nontoxic steel shot is required for waterfowl hunting in all or portions of five coastal counties; nontoxic shot rule is upheld in court

1983 Passage of the Wildlife Conservation Act by the Texas Legislature gives the Texas Parks and Wildlife Commission authority for managing fish and wildlife resources in all Texas counties
Legislature increases the members on the Parks and Wildlife Commission from six to nine
Commission expands the nontoxic shot zone for waterfowl hunting to include all coastal areas and a portion of the prairie area west of Houston

1984 Texas Parks and Wildlife Department initiates Nongame Stamp, Print, and Decal Program to raise funds for endangered and nongame species protection

1988 Texas Parks and Wildlife Department signs a cooperative agreement with U.S. Fish and Wildlife Service in May—under the 1973 Endangered Species Act as amended—for research and management of endangered species
Pittman-Robertson funds for wildlife restriction, including habitat acquired and wildlife research, top $5.1 million in Texas, ranked first among states

Source: Texas Parks and Wildlife Department, Leaflet 9000-27.

Appendix 2

Federal Legislation for Endangered Species

1966 Endangered Species Preservation Act (P.L. 89-669):

a. called upon the Secretary of the Interior to publish a list of species threatened with extinction.
b. authorized funds to conserve, restore, and possibly propagate indigenous fish and wildlife determined to be endangered.

1969 Endangered Species Conservation Act (P.L. 91-135) [repealed in 1973] authorized:
a. listing of foreign species (a worldwide list of species and subspecies) whose importation into the U.S. would be prohibited.
b. possible exceptions but otherwise forbade the purchase or sale of any listed domestic species.
c. $15 million for land acquisition to protect endangered species' habitat.

1973 Endangered Species Act (P.L. 93-205) aimed at:
a. establishing a comprehensive set of regulations for the identification and conservation of endangered fish, wildlife, and plants.
b. listing endangered and threatened species, by the Secretary of Commerce (for certain marine animals) and by the Secretary of the Interior (for all other organisms), on the basis of scientific and commercial data.
c. implementing international treaties and conventions (Convention for the International Trade in Endangered Species – CITES) and providing assistance to foreign countries for conservation programs.
d. designating an area of a species as critical habitat.
e. developing cooperative agreements and programs between states, with federal funding of up to 66.6 percent of costs and 75 percent if two states work jointly for endangered species.
f. directing federal agencies to avoid jeopardizing the existence of a listed species or its habitat.

1978 Amendments to the 1973 Act
a. authorized a seven-member committee to decide on exemptions to federally funded projects that violated the 1973 Act (outcome of Tellico Dam–versus–snail darter controversy).
b. required that the critical habitat of a species be defined at the time the species is listed and that public hearings be held in or near proposed sites.
c. authorized listings to be determined by biological factors.

d. required that the regulation to list be made within two years of the proposal. If not, the proposal is dropped unless new information becomes available.
e. required that the status of each listed species be reviewed every five years.

APPENDIX 3
Endangered Animals and Plants

Common Name	Scientific Name	TPWD[1]	TOES[2]
	MAMMALS		
Whale, blue	*Balaenoptera musculus*	E[3]	NL[6]
Whale, fin	*Balaenoptera physalus*	E	NL
Whale, black right	*Balaena glacialis*	E	NL
Whale, sperm	*Physeter macrocephalus*	E	E
Ferret, black-footed	*Mustela nigripes*	E	E
Jaguar	*Felis onca*	E	E
Jaguarundi	*Felis yagouaroundi*	E	E
Margay	*Felis wiedii*	E	NL
Ocelot	*Felis pardalis*	E	E
Wolf, red	*Canis rufus*	E	E
Wolf, gray	*Canis lupus*	E	E
Bear, black	*Ursus americanus*	E	T[4]
Coati	*Nasua nasua*	E	WL[5]
Manatee	*Trichechus manatus*	E	E
Muskrat, Pecos River	*Ondatra zibethica ripensis*	NL	E
	BIRDS		
Pelican, brown	*Pelecanus occidentalis*	E	E
Stork, wood	*Mycteria americana*	E	T
Eagle, bald	*Haliaeetus leucocephalus*	E	E
Falcon, aplomado	*Falco femoralis*	E	E
Falcon, American peregrine	*Falco peregrinus anatum*	E	E

Prairie chicken, Attwater's greater	*Tympanuchus cupido attwateri*	E	E
Quail, Montezuma	*Cyrtonyx montezumae*	NL	E
Crane, whooping	*Grus americana*	E	E
Plover, piping	*Charadrius melodus*	E	T
Curlew, Eskimo	*Numenius borealis*	E	E
Tern, interior least	*Sterna antillarum athalassos*	E	E
Vireo, black-capped	*Vireo atricapillus*	E	T
Woodpecker, ivory-billed	*Campephilus principalis*	E	E
Woodpecker, red-cockaded	*Picoides borealis*	E	E

REPTILES

Racer, speckled	*Drymobius margaritiferus margaritiferus*	E	T
Snake, Louisiana pine	*Pituophis melanoleucus ruthveni*	E	E
Snake, Concho water	*Nerodia harteri paucimaculata*	E	E
Snake, western smooth green	*Opheodrys vernalis blanchardi*	E	E
Snake, northern cat-eyed	*Leptodeira septentrionalis*	E	T
Turtle, Big Bend mud	*Kinosternon hirtipes murrayi*	E	T
Ridley, Atlantic or Kemp's	*Lepidochelys kempi*	E	E
Hawksbill, Atlantic	*Eretmochelys imbricata imbricata*	E	E
Leatherback	*Dermochelys coriacea*	E	E
Loggerhead	*Caretta caretta*	E	T

AMPHIBIANS

Newt, black-spotted	*Notophthalmus meridionalis*	E	E
Salamander, Blanco blind	*Typhlomolge robusta*	E	T
Salamander, Texas blind	*Typhlomolge rathbuni*	E	T
Siren, Rio Grande lesser	*Siren intermedia texana*	E	E
Toad, Houston	*Bufo houstonensis*	E	E
Frog, white-lipped	*Leptodactylus fragilis*	E	E

FISHES

Paddlefish	*Polyodon spathula*	E	T
Sturgeon, shovelnose	*Scaphirhynchus platorynchus*	E	T
Gambusia, Big Bend	*Gambusia gaigei*	E	E
Gambusia, blotched	*Gambusia senilis*	E	WL
Gambusia, San Marcos	*Gambusia georgei*	E	E
Gambusia, Clear Creek	*Gambusia heterochir*	E	E
Gambusia, Pecos	*Gambusia nobilis*	E	T
Pupfish, Comanche Springs	*Cyprinodon elegans*	E	E
Pupfish, Pecos	*Cyprinodon pecosensis*	T	E
Pupfish, Leon Springs	*Cyprinodon bovinus*	E	E
Darter, fountain	*Etheostoma fonticola*	E	E
Shiner, bluntnose	*Notropis simus*	E	E
Shiner, phantom	*Notropis orca*	E	E
Goby, blackfin	*Gobionellus atripinnis*	E	NL

PLANTS

Bitterweed, Texas	*Hymenoxys texana*	E	E
Bladderpod, white	*Lesquerella pallida*	E	E
Cactus, Tobusch fishhook	*Ancistrocactus tobuschii*	E	E
Cactus, Nellie cory	*Coryphantha minima*	E	E
Cactus, Sneed pincushion	*Coryphantha sneedii sneedii*	E	E
Cactus, Lloyd's hedgehog	*Echinocereus lloydii*	E	E
Cactus, black lace	*Echinocereus reichenbachii* var. *albertii*	E	E
Pitaya, Davis' green	*Echinocereus viridiflorus* var. *davisii*	E	E
Dogweed, ashy	*Dyssodia tephroleuca*	E	E
Frankenia, Johnston's	*Frankenia johnstonii*	E	E
Poppy mallow, Texas	*Callirhoe scabriuscula*	E	E
Ladies' tresses, Navasota	*Spiranthes parksii*	E	E
Rush-pea, slender	*Hoffmanseggia tenella*	E	E
Snowbells, Texas	*Styrax texana*	E	E
Wild rice, Texas	*Zizania texana*	E	E

1 TPWD – Texas Parks and Wildlife Department
2 TOES – Texas Organization for Endangered Species
3 E – Endangered
4 T – Threatened
5 WL – Watch Listed
6 NL – Not Listed

Recent additions: In Fall 1988 federal authorities listed six plants, including the large-fruited sand verbena (*Abronia macrocarpa*) from east Texas, and twelve animal species as endangered. The Mexican long-nosed bat (*Leptonycteris nivalis*), found in Big Bend National Park, was included with the cave invertebrates. The Tooth Cave pseudoscorpion (*Microcreagris texana*), the Tooth Cave spider (*Leptoneta myopica*), the Bee Creek Cave harvestman (*Texella reddelli*), the Tooth Cave ground beetle (*Rhadine persephone*), and the Kretschmarr Cave mold beetle (*Texamaurops reddelli*) are all federally listed as endangered; they are found only in six or fewer dry caves in Travis County, near Austin.

Sources: Texas Parks and Wildlife Department, Leaflet 7100, 1988; Texas Organization for Endangered Species, *Endangered, Threatened and Watch List of Vertebrates of Texas*, 1988; Texas Organization for Endangered Species, *Endangered, Threatened, and Watch Lists of Plants of Texas*, 1987; U.S. Fish and Wildlife Service, *Endangered and Threatened Wildlife and Plants*, 1987.

Appendix 4

Extinct and Extirpated Mammals and Birds of Texas

Species	Status	Distribution	Factors
Merriam's elk	Extinct	Trans-Pecos, Guadalupe Mountains	overhunting?
Mountain sheep	Extirpated	Trans-Pecos mountains	overhunting, bluetongue disease, fencing
Red wolf	Extirpated from the wild	central, east, and coastal Texas	hunting, poisoning, hybridization

Gray wolf	Extirpated	west Texas	hunting, poisoning
Grizzly bear	Extirpated	Trans-Pecos	shot (one record)
Black-footed ferret	Extirpated	west Texas	poisoning of prairie dogs
Jaguar	Extirpated	south and east Texas	overhunting, habitat loss
Bison	Extirpated from the wild	west, central, and east Texas	overhunting
West Indian manatee	Extirpated	coastal Texas	overhunting, incompatible with boat traffic
Sharp-tailed grouse	Extirpated	Panhandle	overhunting
Passenger pigeon	Extinct	central and east Texas	overhunting
Carolina parakeet	Extinct	central and east Texas	overhunting
Ivory-billed woodpecker	Extinct	east Texas	habitat loss and hunting

To complete your set of Texas Monthly Press field guides, check your local bookstore, use the order form below, or call toll free 1-800-288-3288.

P.O. Box 1569 Austin, Texas 78767

QUANTITY	TITLE		PRICE
________	A FIELD GUIDE TO ARCHEOLOGICAL SITES OF TEXAS, Nunley	$11.95 pb	________
________	A FIELD GUIDE TO BIRDS OF THE BIG BEND, Wauer	$9.95 pb	________
________	A FIELD GUIDE TO FOSSILS OF TEXAS, Finsley	$16.95 pb	________
________	A FIELD GUIDE TO REPTILES & AMPHIBIANS OF TEXAS, Garrett & Barker	$14.95 pb	________
________	A FIELD GUIDE TO STONE ARTIFACTS OF TEXAS INDIANS, Turner & Hester	$12.95 pb	________
________	A FIELD GUIDE TO TEXAS SNAKES, Tennant	$14.95 pb	________
________	A FIELD GUIDE TO TEXAS TREES, Simpson	$16.95 pb	________
________	A FIELD GUIDE TO WILDLIFE IN TEXAS AND THE SOUTHWEST, Miller	$14.95 pb	________
________	ENDANGERED SPECIES, Doughty & Parmenter	$9.95 pb	________
________	TEXAS PHOTO SAFARIS, Miller	$14.95 pb	________
________	Current catalog of all Texas Monthly Press books	$2.00	________
		Subtotal	________
		Texas residents add 7% sales tax	________
		Postage and handling	$2.50
		TOTAL	________

Name ____

Address ____

City ____________________ State ____________ Zip ____________

Please check ☐ Check / money order ☐ Visa ☐ Mastercard

Account # ____________________ Exp. date ____________

Name on credit card ________________________________

Signature ____

Please allow 2-4 weeks delivery

SP02